Transitional
Elements

D0583997

Edwin M. Larsen

University of Wisconsin

1965

W. A. BENJAMIN, INC.   New York   Amsterdam

TRANSITIONAL ELEMENTS

Library of Congress Catalog Card Number 65–11526
Manufactured in the United States of America

*The manuscript was put into production on August 4, 1964;
this volume was published on April 26, 1965*

W. A. BENJAMIN, INC.
New York, New York 10016

Editor's Foreword

THE TEACHING OF INTRODUCTORY CHEMISTRY becomes each day a more challenging and rewarding task as subject matter becomes more diverse and more complex and as the high school preparation of the student improves. These challenges have evoked a number of responses; this series of monographs for general chemistry is one such. It is an experiment in the teaching of chemistry which recognizes a number of the problems that confront those who select textbooks and teach chemistry. First of all, it is recognized that no single book can physically encompass all of the various aspects of chemistry that all instructors collectively deem important. Second, it is admitted that no single author is capable of writing authoritatively on *all* of the topics that are included in everybody's list of what constitutes introductory chemistry. Finally, it recognizes the instructor's right to choose those topics which he considers to be important without having to apologize for having omitted large parts of an extensive textbook.

This volume, then, is one of approximately fifteen in the General Chemistry Monograph Series, each written by one or more highly qualified persons very familiar with the current status of the subject by virtue of research in it, but also conversant with the problems associated with teaching the subject matter to beginning students. Each volume deals broadly with one of the subdivisions of general chemistry or areas directly impinging on it and constitutes a complete entity, far more comprehensive in coverage than is permitted by the limitations of the standard one-volume text. Taken together these volumes provide a range of topics from which the individual instructor can easily select those which will provide for his class an appropriate coverage of the material he considers most important.

Furthermore, coverage of a number of topics only recently being considered for introductory chemistry courses, such as thermodynamics, molecular spectroscopy, reaction kinetics and mechanism, atomic spectroscopy, photochemistry, and biochemistry is or will soon be available. In every instance a modern structural point of view has been adopted. The emphasis is on general principles and unifying theory, but with adequate reference to experiments.

These materials will have other uses also; selected volumes can be used to enrich the more conventional course of study by providing readily available inexpensive supplements to standard texts. They should also prove valuable to students in other areas of the physical and biological sciences needing supplementary information in the field of chemistry pertinent to their own special interests. Thus, students of biology should find the monographs on biochemistry, organic chemistry, coordination chemistry, and reaction kinetics particularly useful. Beginning students in physics and meteorology will find the monographs on thermodynamics and atomic structure rewarding. Teachers of elementary science will also find these invaluable aids to bringing them up to date in the various branches of chemistry. The monograph on nuclei and radioactivity should prove useful to anyone interested in the application of radioisotopes to experimental problems.

Each of these monographs has several features which make them especially useful as aids to teaching. These include a large number of solved examples and problems for the student, a glossary of technical terms, and copious illustrations.

It is hoped that titles will continue to be added as new areas come into the purview of introductory chemistry. Suggestions for additions to the series will be welcomed by the editor.

RUSSELL JOHNSEN

Tallahassee, Florida
April 1965

Preface

THIS BOOK is an introduction to the chemistry of the transitional elements for the student in chemistry or the allied sciences. It can be used to supplement the normal second-semester lecture material or be used in an intermediate course in inorganic chemistry. As much of the chemistry as possible is related to the elementary principles of chemistry usually introduced in a first-year course for majors. Sufficient discussion of the principles is included to make the narrative readable and to provide continuity. However, the principles are not generally developed in detail within this book and, therefore, the student is expected to have other sources available in which to study the principles in more depth and rigor. The student will also need an introduction to organic chemistry to assimilate the material on coordination chemistry and organometallic compounds.

The emphasis is on the general types of reactions which the transitional elements undergo. For example, it seems important that the student be able to answer the following questions when he dissolves a compound in water: How strong an acid is the cation? To what pH can the solution be taken before the hydroxide precipitates? To what extent do the anion and cation interact to form associated species? Are the aqueous species stable with respect to oxidation-reduction by water? Similar questions can be raised with respect to the stability of the solid state: Are the simple binary compounds stable thermally? If decomposition occurs, is it by disproportionation or decomposition to a lower oxidation state compound? Sufficient detailed chemical information is included to support the general conclusions. There is a danger that students will conclude that all the chemistry falls into neat categories. I hope that sufficient uncorrelated material has been included to dispel this idea, but the instructor should make certain that the student understands that chemistry is still an experimental science—witness, for example, the discovery of cyclopentadienyl transitional metal compounds in 1951 and that of xenon tetrafluoride in 1963.

I wish to acknowledge that I have drawn on many sources for much of the data included in this book. These have been tabulated in the Appendix under "Reference Materials." I also wish to acknowledge the importance of the many informal discussions with my former colleague, Professor E. L. King, now of the University of Colorado, over the period of years that we cooperatively developed a senior inorganic course, from which much of the organizational pattern of this book is drawn. Also, my colleague Dr. Richard Fenske contributed significantly through discussions of certain portions of the manuscript. I am also indebted to my present graduate students Messrs. C. A. Adams, P. Arvedsen, E. Homeier, and G. McDonald and Misses M. North, and J. Sukup, all of whom contributed to this manuscript by compiling data, making drawings, and contributing constructive suggestions.

EDWIN M. LARSEN

Madison, Wisconsin
August 1964

Contents

Introduction

IRON, COPPER, SILVER, AND GOLD were among the elements known to early man. Actually, we classify these elements with the elements known as the transitional elements, a large group of metallic elements having certain similar chemical and physical properties, which includes nickel, chromium, titanium, and platinum in addition to those named above. Most of the transitional elements are much less familiar than these and not too many years ago were laboratory curiosities. The demand for materials of special qualities in the nuclear and space age has focussed attention on the properties of the transitional elements and already uses of great technical importance have been found for many of them.

The transitional metals in general are more dense and higher melting than nontransitional metals such as calcium and sodium. They form many alloys and also binary compounds such as oxides, nitrides, and carbides, some of which are particularly high melting and corrosion resistant. They show a wide range of oxidation states and thus are an important source of oxidizing and reducing agents. The metals, and especially compounds of the lower oxidation states, have catalytic properties and are used in organic syntheses. They are particularly important, for example, in the polymerization of ethylene to give polyethylene. These elements also have the property of forming many complex compounds with a wide variety of organic ligands and, in many instances, are known to play an important role in biological processes.

The increased activity in this field has resulted in a large volume of newly published literature. This small book is not intended as a detailed résumé, but rather as an introduction to further reading.

I

The Properties of the Transitional Elements

THIS CHAPTER is devoted to a discussion of the physical properties used in correlating the chemical properties of the transitional elements. This includes electronic structures, sizes of atoms and ions, and ionization potentials. Also included is a discussion of color and paramagnetism. The chemistry of the transitional elements in solution, in the solid state, and in complex ions is developed in succeeding chapters.

1–1 DEFINITION

The transitional elements are characterized by participation of d orbitals in chemical bond formation. The transitional elements are defined therefore as those elements, the atoms or ions of which contain partially filled d orbitals. This includes the elements from scandium to copper, yttrium to silver, and lanthanum to gold. A fourth transitional series starts with actinium, but is not complete. In terms of their presently known chemistry, zinc, cadmium, and mercury are not included by this definition. Those elements which have an incomplete f as well as an incomplete d orbital are called

1-1 The periodic table

	IA	IIA	IIIB	IVB	VB	VIB	VIIB	VIII			IB	IIB	IIIA	IVA	VA	VIA	VIIA	
	1 **H** 1.008																	2 **He** 4.003
Period 2 (2)	3 **Li** 6.940	4 **Be** 9.013											5 **B** 10.82	6 **C** 12.010	7 **N** 14.008	8 **O** 16.0000	9 **F** 19.00	10 **Ne** 20.183
Period 3 (2 8)	11 **Na** 22.991	12 **Mg** 24.32											13 **Al** 26.98	14 **Si** 28.09	15 **P** 30.98	16 **S** 32.066	17 **Cl** 35.457	18 **Ar** 39.944
Period 4 (2 8 8)	19 **K** 39.100	20 **Ca** 40.08	21 **Sc** 44.96	22 **Ti** 47.90	23 **V** 50.95	24 **Cr** 52.01	25 **Mn** 54.94	26 **Fe** 55.85	27 **Co** 58.94	28 **Ni** 58.71	29 **Cu** 63.54	30 **Zn** 65.38	31 **Ga** 69.72	32 **Ge** 72.60	33 **As** 74.91	34 **Se** 78.96	35 **Br** 79.916	36 **Kr** 83.80
Period 5 (2 8 18 8)	37 **Rb** 85.48	38 **Sr** 87.63	39 **Y** 88.92	40 **Zr** 91.22	41 **Nb** 92.91	42 **Mo** 95.95	43 **Tc*** [99]	44 **Ru** 101.1	45 **Rh** 102.91	46 **Pd** 106.4	47 **Ag** 107.880	48 **Cd** 112.41	49 **In** 114.82	50 **Sn** 118.70	51 **Sb** 121.76	52 **Te** 127.61	53 **I** 126.91	54 **Xe** 131.30
Period 6 (2 8 18 18 8)	55 **Cs** 132.91	56 **Ba** 137.36	57 to 71 **La** 138.9	72 **Hf** 178.50	73 **Ta** 180.95	74 **W** 183.86	75 **Re** 186.22	76 **Os** 190.2	77 **Ir** 192.2	78 **Pt** 195.09	79 **Au** 197.0	80 **Hg** 200.61	81 **Tl** 204.39	82 **Pb** 207.21	83 **Bi** 209.00	84 **Po*** 210	85 **At*** [210]	86 **Rn*** 222
Period 7 (2 8 18 32 18 8)	87 **Fr*** [223]	88 **Ra*** 226.05	89 **Ac*** 227	90 **Th*** 232.05	91 92 to 103 **Pa*** 231													

4f series

58 **Ce** 140.13	59 **Pr** 140.92	60 **Nd** 144.27	61 **Pm*** [145]	62 **Sm** 150.35	63 **Eu** 152.0	64 **Gd** 157.26	65 **Tb** 158.93	66 **Dy** 162.51	67 **Ho** 164.94	68 **Er** 167.27	69 **Tm** 168.94	70 **Yb** 173.04	71 **Lu** 174.99

5f series

91 **Pa*** 231	92 **U*** 238.07	93 **Np*** [237]	94 **Pu*** [242]	95 **Am*** [243]	96 **Cm*** [248]	97 **Bk*** [247]	98 **Cf*** [251]	99 **Es***	100 **Fm***	101 **Md***	102 **—***	103 **Lw***

* All isotopes are radioactive.
[ ] Indicates mass number of longest known half-life.
Note: The small figures at far left show electron distribution in preceding nobel gas.

2

the inner-transitional elements. These include the elements from cerium to lutetium, the 4*f* or, more commonly, the Lanthanides, and the elements from uranium to lawrencium, the 5*f* series or, more commonly, the Actinides. The four transitional series and the two inner-transitional series are outlined on the periodic table (Figure 1–1).

1–2 A BRIEF REVIEW OF ATOMIC STRUCTURE

The present-day philosophy of the nature of matter does not allow the description of an atom in terms of the exact position of the electron in a fixed orbit. It does, however, allow a description in terms of the probability of finding an electron in a given volume of space. The dual nature of matter, either as particles or waves, allows the application of the mathematics developed for the description of matter waves to the problem of atomic structure. The properties of a single electron about a positive nucleus are defined in an equation in which the energy of the electron and its wave property (a function of the amplitude is used) are related. Such a wave function is called an atomic orbital. It is common practice to say that the electron resides in the orbital. There is one orbital of lowest energy which constitutes the ground state for a one electron system. Other orbitals have particular higher values of energy. The particular values (levels) permitted are determined by the wave equation. There are three index numbers, which are used to classify and refer to the orbitals. These are symbolized by n, l, and m_l. The principal quantum number n is always a positive integer. The azimuthal quantum number l may have a value of zero, or any positive integer up to $n - 1$, while the magnetic quantum number m_l can have any integral value from $-l$ to $+l$. The number of possible orbitals thus defined are shown in Table 1–1. (Since orbitals with l greater than three do not enter into ordinary chemical behavior, we do not include in the table all possible orbitals for n greater than four.) A fourth property, electron spin (m_s), classifies the type of electron in the orbital. There are only two possible types, those with clockwise and those with counterclockwise spin ($m_s + \frac{1}{2}$ or $- \frac{1}{2}$). In multielectron elements, the general rule

Table 1-1
Quantum Number Combinations

n	1	2		3			4				5				6			7		
l	0	0	1	0	1	2	0	1	2	3	0	1	2	3	0	1	2	0	1	2
m_l	0	0	±1	0	±1	±2	0	±1	±2	±3	0	±1	±2	±3	0	±1	±2	0	±1	±2
			0		0	±1		0	±1	±2		0	±1	±2		0	±1		0	±1
						0			0	±1			0	±1			0			0
										0				0						
m_s	±	±	±	±	±	±	±	±	±	±	±	±	±	±	±	±	±	±	±	±
Number of Orbitals	1	1	3	1	3	5	1	3	5	7	1	3	5	7	1	3	5	1	3	5
Symbol	s	s	p	s	p	d	s	p	d	f	s	p	d	f	s	p	d	s	p	d
Electron Capacity	2	2	6	2	6	10	2	6	10	14	2	6	10	14	2	6	10	2	6	10

4

(Pauli Exclusion Principle) is that no two electrons may have all four quantum numbers the same. Hence, the index numbers that classify the orbitals are also sufficient to classify the electrons, with the addition of the spin quantum number.

For the purpose of writing electron notations, orbitals of each l value are identified by a letter. Thus orbitals of $l = 0$ are s orbitals, $l = 1$, p orbitals, $l = 2$, d orbitals, and $l = 3$, f orbitals. The l values actually are related to the number of units of angular momentum the electron possesses in the given orbital. The sublevels of l are identified by sign as well as magnitude as follows: for p electrons, m_l has the values of 1, 0, -1; for d electrons m_l has values of 2, 1, 0, -1, -2; and for f electrons 3, 2, 1, 0, -1, -2, -3. We also see from Table 1–1 that the quantum number combinations determine that d orbitals do not appear until $n = 3$, f orbitals when $n = 4$, and that there are three p orbitals, five d orbitals, and seven f orbitals.

Some physical significance can be assigned to the quantum numbers in terms of shape, size, and orientation of the orbitals

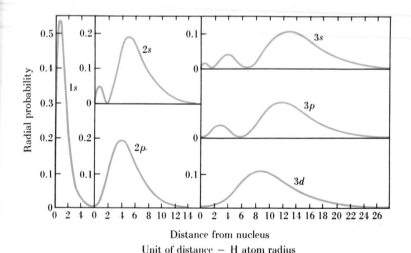

1–2   **Radial probability distribution plot for 1s, 2s, 2p, 3p, and 3d hydrogen-like orbitals.**

with respect to one another in a magnetic field. The quantum number n is related to the energy and the volume of the geometrical figure in which the electron has a high probability of being found; l is related to the shape of the geometrical figure in which the electron has a high probability of being found. The quantum number m_l, by the relationship $(2l + 1)$, defines the number of sublevels and their orientation with respect to one another in a magnetic field.

The probability of finding an electron in a given volume of space is a function of three variables, which in polar coordinates are the distance from the nucleus r, and two angles Θ and Φ. A

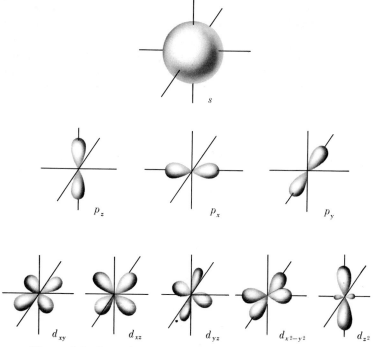

Figure 1-3 Boundary surfaces showing the angular dependence of the probability (0.95) of finding an electron therein.

graph of the probability against r, Θ, and Φ would require four co-ordinates. It is normal practice, therefore, to make two plots, one of which is a plot of the probability against r, or the so-called radial probability plot. Figure 1–2 shows such a plot for the $1s$, $2s$, $3s$, $2p$, $3p$, and $3d$ orbitals of the hydrogen atom. Observe that the d orbital does not penetrate as close to the nucleus as does the p or s orbital.

The second is a plot of the probability against the two angles Θ and Φ. In such a plot there are generated surfaces within which the electron has a high probability of being found. Because this volume cannot be defined with a probability of 1, dimensions must be used for which the probability is somewhat smaller; a probability of 0.95 is frequently used. The geometrical figures which describe the angular dependence of the probability for s, p, and d electrons appear in Figure 1–3. Note that the axes of these volumes are labeled in Cartesian coordinates, and that the volumes are named according to their position with respect to the axes. (Figure 1–4 shows the relationship between polar coordinates and Cartesian coordinates.) The d_{xy}, d_{xz}, d_{yx} surfaces have lobes in the plane described by the respective axes, but oriented between the

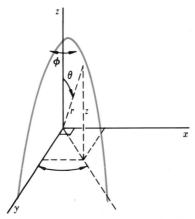

Figure 1–4   The relationship of polar coordinates to cartesian coordinates.

axes rather than along them. In contrast, the $d_{x^2-y^2}$, and the d_{z^2} surfaces lie along the axes. The figures for f surfaces are still more complicated and are not given here.

1-3   ELECTRONIC CONFIGURATIONS OF ATOMS AND IONS

The atoms of multielectron elements are built up, figuratively speaking, by using orbitals described for the single electron of the hydrogen atom. The utilization of hydrogen-like orbitals is an approximation, because it is not possible to make rigorous calculations for the interactions of the individual electrons with one another.

In progressing from one atomic number to the next by adding a proton to the nucleus in the hypothetical building-up process, an electron is added to the extranuclear structure. The electron occupies the orbital which gives an electron arrangement of the lowest possible energy for the whole atom. Each orbital may be doubly occupied as permitted by the Pauli Exclusion Principle, but this does not occur until each orbital of a given energy level contains one electron. For example, the d^4 configuration would be represented by, $\downarrow$ $\downarrow$ $\downarrow$ $\downarrow$ __.

To develop an order of orbital occupancy it is necessary to know what arrangement of electrons will give an atom of lowest energy content for each atomic number. This information can be obtained from the type of data in Figure 1-5, where the binding energy of an electron in a given orbital is plotted as a function of atomic number. This binding energy at each atomic number is defined as the energy change the whole atom undergoes when an electron of a given orbital is removed. The plot in Figure 1-5 is abridged to show only those atomic numbers of particular interest to the following discussion.

For the elements of atomic number 1 through 18, the order of the binding energy is $n = 1 > 2 > 3$ and within the sublevels, $s > p$. The description of the resulting electron arrangements follows a system of electron notation, such as $1s^2\ 2s^2\ 2p^6$, where the coefficient is the quantum number n and the letter is determined by the quantum number l being s, p, d, or f for $l = 0, 1, 2$ or 3.

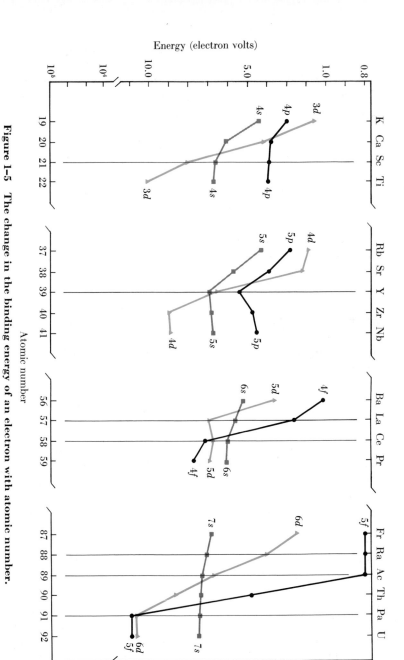

Figure 1-5 The change in the binding energy of an electron with atomic number.

The superscript indicates the number of electrons in the orbital; the sum of the superscripts equals the number of electrons in the atom or ion. This notation does not describe unambiguously the energy state of the atom, for it does not tell how the spin and the orbital motions of the electrons interact.

The convention for writing the electron notation of transitional elements will be always to write the number of "ns" electrons last. There are two reasons for this: (1) the net effect of ionization, with few exceptions, is the loss of an s electron; (2) from the radial probability plots, the "ns" electrons have a higher probability of being far from the nucleus than do the inner-shell electrons, thus establishing the s orbitals as the "boundary" orbitals in the neutral atom (Figure 1–6).

The electron arrangement for element of atomic number 18 is $1s^2 \, 2s^2 \, 2p^6 \, 3s^2 \, 3p^6$. Now, with potassium (atomic number 19) a new situation arises. Will the electron configuration beyond the argon core be $3d^1$, $4s^1$, or $4p^1$? We need consider this electron only, because the completed levels are assumed to remain undisturbed. From experimental data we know that the potassium atom with the configuration $4s^1$ is of lower energy than a potassium atom with either the $4p^1$ or $3d^1$ configuration. This is in accordance with the data plotted in Figure 1–5. The other arrangements are of higher energy and are said to represent "excited" states. For calcium (atomic number 20), the same kind of information shows that the $4s^2$ configuration is the ground-state electron description of the neutral gaseous atom.

Now another problem arises at atomic number 21. Because the capacity of the $4s$ orbital has been reached, the electron notations for scandium must include some other orbital. Some possible notations are $3d^3$, $3d^2 \, 4s^1$, $3d^1 \, 4s^2$, $3d^1 \, 4s^1 \, 4p^1$, $3d^1 \, 4s^1 \, 5s^1$, and $3d^2 \, 4p^1$ among others. Figure 1–7 shows a simplified relationship of these electron arrangements to their energy for the scandium atom. Thus $3d^1 \, 4s^2$ is the ground-state arrangement, and the other arrangements represent excited states. In continuing the hypothetical build-up of atoms, the filling of the d orbitals, once started, continues until the capacity is reached. This feature of electron arrangements reappears at regular intervals throughout the periodic table and is characteristic of the transitional elements. The

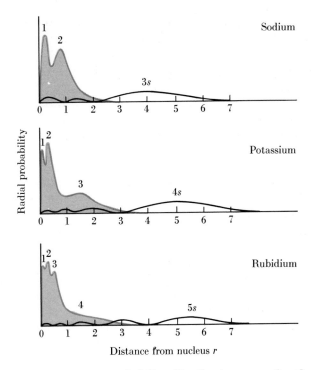

Figure 1-6 Radial probability distribution curve for the neutral atoms of sodium, potassium, and rubidium, showing the core electrons by the shaded area and the valence electrons by the area under the single line.

configurations for the neutral gaseous atoms of the 3d elements are given in Table 1–2.

After completion of the 4p level and the introduction of the 5s electrons, the electron arrangement $4d^1 5s^2$ appears at atomic number 39. This arrangement is of lower energy than one involving the 5p orbital. As in the case of the 3d elements, the $(n-1)\,d^n ns^2$ configuration constitutes the ground-state arrangement for the atoms throughout the rest of the period. The electron configurations for the neutral gaseous atoms of the 4d series are also listed in Table 1–2.

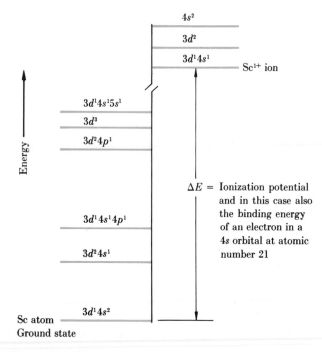

Figure 1–7   The ground states and excited states of the scandium atom and ion (simplified).

After filling the $5p$ and $6s$ orbitals, the $5d^1\,6s^2$ arrangement appears at atomic number 57.   In effect, the next electron is a $5d$ electron rather than a $6p$ (Figure 1–5).   Now, at atomic number 58, cerium, the relationship becomes more complex, with the $4f$ orbital, which had been previously bypassed, coming into use.   For cerium, the configuration corresponding to the electron notation $4f^25s^25p^65d^06s^2$ is of lowest energy, and the net effect is that the $4f$ orbital begins to fill.   This continues until the seven $4f$ orbitals have been filled to capacity.   After the completion of the $4f$ orbital, the $5d$ orbital occupancy continues until filled.   The electron configuration for the neutral gaseous atoms of $5d$ and $4f$ elements also appear in Table 1–2.

Table 1-2

Electron Configurations of the Transitional and Inner-Transitional Elements

Sc	21—$3d^14s^2$	Y	39—$4d^15s^2$	La	57—$5d^16s^2$	Ac	89—$5f^06d^17s^2$
Ti	22—$3d^24s^2$	Zr	40—$4d^25s^2$	Hf	72—$5d^26s^2$	Th	90—$5f^06d^27s^2$
V	23—$3d^34s^2$	Nb	41—$4d^45s^1$	Ta	73—$5d^36s^2$	—	104—$5f^{14}6d^27s^2$
Cr	24—$3d^54s^1$	Mo	42—$4d^55s^1$	W	74—$5d^46s^2$		
Mn	25—$3d^54s^2$	Tc	43—$4d^55s^1$	Re	75—$5d^56s^2$		
Fe	26—$3d^64s^2$	Ru	44—$4d^75s^1$	Os	76—$5d^66s^2$		
Co	27—$3d^74s^2$	Rh	45—$4d^85s^1$	Ir	77—$5d^76s^2$		
Ni	28—$3d^84s^2$	Pd	46—$4d^{10}5s^0$	Pt	78—$5d^96s^1$		
Cu	29—$3d^{10}4s^1$	Ag	47—$4d^{10}5s^1$	Au	79—$5d^{10}6s^1$		

Ce	58	$(4f^25d^06s^2)$		
Pr	59	$(4f^35d^06s^2)$		
Nd	60	$4f^45d^06s^2$		
Pm	61	$(4f^55d^06s^2)$	Pa	91	$(5f^26d^17s^2)$
Sm	62	$4f^65d^06s^2$	U	92	$5f^36d^17s^2$
Eu	63	$4f^75d^06s^2$	Np	93	$(5f^46d^17s^2)$
Gd	64	$4f^75d^16s^2$	Pu	94	$(5f^56d^17s^2)$
Tb	65	$(4f^95d^06s^2)$	Am	95	$(5f^76d^07s^2)$
Dy	66	$(4f^{10}5d^06s^2)$	Cm	96	$(5f^76d^17s^2)$
Ho	67	$(4f^{11}5d^06s^2)$	Bk	97	$(5f^86d^17s^2)$
Er	68	$(4f^{12}5d^06s^2)$	Cf	98	$(5f^96d^17s^2)$
Tm	69	$4f^{13}5d^06s^2$	Es	99	$(5f^{10}6d^17s^2)$
Yb	70	$4f^{14}5d^06s^2$	Fm	100	$(5f^{11}6d^17s^2)$
Lu	71	$4f^{14}5d^16s^2$	Md	101	$(5f^{12}6d^17s^2)$
			—	102	$(5f^{14}6d^07s^2)$
			Lw	103	$(5f^{14}6d^17s^2)$

The introduction of the first $6d$ electron occurs at actinium, atomic number 89, thus starting the $6d$ transitional series. Now again, as with the $4f$ series, the binding energy of the $5f$ orbital (Figure 1–5) crosses the $6d$ level to give electron configurations of $5f^n6s^26p^66d^17s^2$. However, this point does not occur at the same relative position in the $5f$ series as it does in the $4f$ series. In its ground state, the cerium atom has $4f$ electrons, but thorium does not have $5f$ electrons in its ground state. The $5f$ electrons are known to first appear in the ground state of uranium. In Figure 1–5, the binding energies are drawn as though the f filling started with element 91, protactinium. Regardless of the possible disagreement on the starting point of the filling of the $5f$ orbitals, there seems to be general agreement that the filling of the $5f$ orbitals continues once it has started and that with element 103, the inner-transitional series comes to an end. Presumably, the filling of the $6d$ orbitals is resumed with element 104. The external electron configurations for the neutral gaseous atoms of the Actinide elements also appear in Table 1–2.

It is to be noted that the electronic configurations for the ground state, as determined experimentally by spectroscopists, do not always have two s electrons. Sometimes it appears that one or even two of the s electrons are "borrowed" by the d or f orbitals to give a configuration other than that obtained by the ideal building-up process. This irregularity occurs particularly at the atomic number preceding the half-filling or complete filling of d or f orbitals. In the $4d$ series, however, it is almost the rule rather than the exception. Note also that for yttrium and actinium (Figure 1–5) the binding energy for the $(n − 1)d$ orbital is higher than for the ns orbital, the reverse of the scandium and lanthanum case. This is of no consequence chemically, however, because this configuration only bears on the M^{1+} ion configuration which is not obtained in chemical reactions.

With sufficient input of energy an electron is removed to convert an atom into an ion. A variety of electron arrangements can be written for an ion also, but of these, only one is the ground-state configuration for the ion. Thus the electron notation for the ground state of the scandium atom is $3d^1 4s^2$, and that for the Sc^{1+} ion is $3d^1 4s^1$. Other electron notations (Figure 1–7) represent excited states of the ion. The net effect of this ionization process is the loss of an s electron, and the energy required for this process is the binding energy of an electron in the $4s$ orbital at atomic number 21. For M^{2+} ions and higher, there is no exception to the general rule that s electrons are lost first in the ionization process. Thus Ti $3d^2 4s^2$, $Ti^{2+} 3d^2 4s^0$, $Ti^{3+} 3d^1 4s^0$, and $Ti^{4+} 3d^0 4s^0$. The M^{3+} ions of the inner-transitional elements show no d or s electrons in the ground state, and the electrons of the $5s^2 5p^6$ and $6s^2 6p^6$ orbitals remain intact; thus Ce^{3+} $4f^1 5s^2 5p^6 5d^0 6s^0$ and Ce^{4+} $4f^0 5s^2 5p^6 5d^0 6d^0$, while U^{3+} is $5f^3 6s^2 6p^6 6d^0 7s^0$, and U^{4+} is $5f^2 6s^2 6p^6 6d^0 7s^0$.

1–4 THE FILLING OF d AND f ORBITALS— LIGAND FIELD THEORY

In isolated gaseous atoms or ions of a given element, the five d orbitals are all of the same energy. In the solid state or in solution, however, the d orbitals are subject to the charge fields of adjacent ions or dipoles of neutral molecules. The net result is to raise the energy of the orbitals and further to split them into different energies. How the orbitals are split in energy depends upon the number of groups (normally called ligands) bonded to the central metal ion, the symmetry of the set of ligands, and the nature of the ligands. Although the separation is calculated mathematically, an intuitive approach yields a qualitative answer. This is based on the principle that the orbitals of the central metal ion which are directed along the axes on which the ligand atoms or ions reside will be raised in energy, while those which are directed away from the ligands will be reduced in energy. The axes in Figure 1–8 are drawn and labelled with the same convention as those in Figure 1–3, so that the orientation of the orbitals can be compared to the symmetry of the set of ligands and the energy separation of the orbitals. The five d orbitals are split into two energies in the tetrahedral case—two orbitals of low energy, and three of higher energy. The octahedral case has the two groups of orbitals inverted. For the square planar symmetry, the orbitals are split further, with the relative position of the d_{z^2} orbital still an unsettled question. The magnitude of the energy separation between orbitals for a given metal ion with different ligands but the same symmetry is smaller for H_2O and OH (weak-field) than for CN^- (Strong-field). The magnitude of the energy separation between orbitals differs from tetrahedral to octahedral to square planar; for instance, the separation Δ with ligands in the tetrahedral symmetry is only $\frac{4}{9}$ that of the energy separation between orbitals for the same ligands in octahedral symmetry around the same metal ion.

The strength of the ligand field determines how the d^n electrons are distributed in the orbitals. The rule is that the orbitals of lowest energy are occupied singly before any orbital is doubly occupied or before a higher orbital is occupied. For example, in

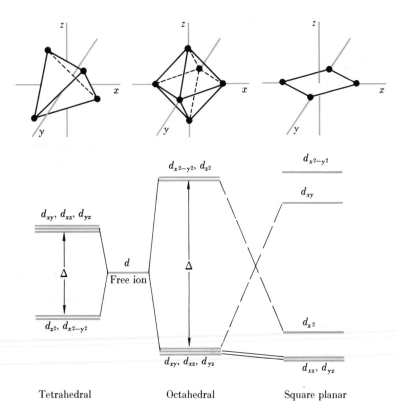

Figure 1-8 *d* **orbital splitting in tetrahedral, octahedral, and square planar ligand fields.**

the case of octahedral symmetry, the electron distribution in the presence of a weak-field ligand is different than the distribution in the presence of a strong-field ligand for only configurations d^4 to d^7 (Figure 1-9). The choice is dependent upon the relative energies of the alternate arrangements. Pairing up of electrons requires energy, and the choice is whether it is less expensive energywise to occupy a higher level singly or a lower level doubly. The

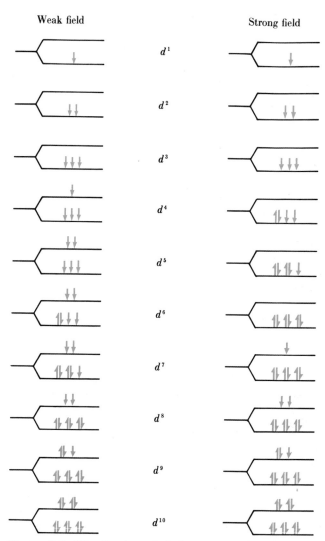

Figure 1-9 Distribution of d electrons in d^1 to d^{10} configurations in octahedral sites for weak-field and strong-field ligands.

choice for a weak-field ligand is to occupy the higher level singly. The choice for a strong-field ligand is to occupy the lower level doubly, because the energy separation between the lowest level and the next highest level is too great.

In ions of the lanthanides and actinide periods, the $(n - 1)f$ electrons are not disturbed by the adjacent charge fields because they are shielded by the ns^2np^6 electrons. Therefore, the rule to apply is that the electrons achieve maximum occupancy before pairing up; thus Gd^{3+} $4f^7$ can be symbolized as ↓ ↓ ↓ ↓ ↓ ↓ ↓.

1–5   RADII—METALLIC, IONIC, AND COVALENT

The radius of an isolated atom is directly proportional to the square of the quantum number n and inversely proportional to the atomic number Z, $r \propto n^2/Z$. Thus, in a period of given n, the atomic dimensions decrease with an increase in Z across the period and increase with an increase of n down a group. In the d and f

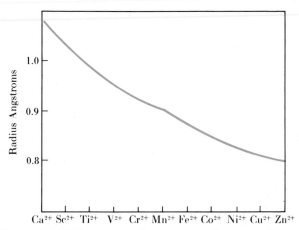

Figure 1–10   The expected variation of ionic radius of gaseous ions of the 3d transitional elements versus effective nuclear charge.

filling, the *ns* boundary electrons "see" the increase in nuclear charge because the *d* and *f* electrons do not penetrate close to the nucleus and, therefore, only partially shield the valence electrons from the increase in nuclear charge. The expected size trend with atomic number for the 3*d* elements is plotted in Figure 1–10.

Radii of atoms and ions in solids are determined by x-ray diffraction measurements of internuclear distances. These dimensions are sensitive to several variables including the number of equidistant nearest neighbors, the valency, and the nature of the bond. The data can be compared within a row or group of the periodic table as long as these variables remain reasonably constant.

Metallic Radii

A solid metal may be considered to be made up of spheres packed together as efficiently as possible (Chapter 3). Because all the atoms of a metal are the same and all the nearest neighbors are equidistant, one-half of the internuclear distance may be taken as the atomic radius. These data are plotted in Figure 1–11 and tabulated in Table A-4 of the Appendix. Note that the data show the expected trend except that there is a levelling off and then a slight increase in size with the addition of the eighth electron. That the expected trend does not continue is evidence of the fact that in the solid state, the valence electrons of neighboring atoms interact to effectively occupy more space than expected.

It should be noted that the difference between atomic radii of the 3*d* and 4*d* elements amounts to more than 0.1 *A*, but the difference between the atomic radii of the 4*d* and 5*d* elements is only 0.02 *A*. This can be accounted for by the fact that the 3*d* and 4*d* periods are followed by filling of the *p* orbitals, while the filling of the 5*d* orbitals is interrupted by the introduction of the 4*f* level electrons. The contraction in size which the elements of the 4*f* period undergo is called the Lanthanide contraction (Figure 1–11). Unlike the *d* contraction, the *f* contraction continues throughout the entire period, because the *f* electrons do not get involved in the metallic bonding. The net result of this contraction is that element 68, erbium, has an atomic radius comparable to that of element 39,

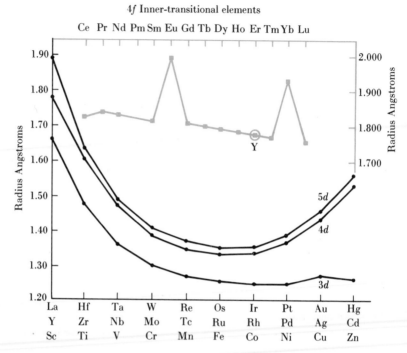

Figure 1–11 **The metallic radii of the transitional elements and inner-transitional elements versus atomic number.**

yttrium. Also, the first element following the completion of the $4f$ period, element 72, hafnium, has an atomic radius almost identical with that of zirconium, element 40. This effect is found throughout the rest of the $5d$ period and results in the small size differential between the atoms of the $4d$ and $5d$ periods. .

In the $4f$ period, the metallic radii for europium and ytterbium are out of line compared with the other f electron elements. Note that in these two cases no d electrons appear in the electron configurations which have one-half filled and completely filled f levels, respectively; $4f^7 5s^2 5p^6 5d^0 6s^2$ and $4f^{14} 5s^2 5p^6 5d^0 6s^2$. In this respect these two elements have configurations and sizes more comparable to a Group II element like barium than a Group III element like lanthanum.

Ionic Radii

Unlike the metals, the ions which make up a solid are not all alike. To establish a set of ionic radii, one ion is taken as a standard, and the other radii are derived by subtracting the radius of the standard ion from the experimentally determined internuclear distance. The ion most often used as the standard is the oxide ion, although on occasions the fluoride ion has been used. The dimension of the standard ion is derived from a structure in which the ions are close packed (see Section 3–1) so that the internuclear distance of the ions which touch can be obtained. Certain silicates have been used for this information. As in the case of metals then, one-half the distance is taken as the radius of the oxide ion. Unfortunately, not all investigators agree on the size of the oxide ion, and the values employed vary from 1.35 to 1.20 A. Therefore values of the same ion vary from one source to another.

As one might expect, some of the trends found among metallic radii are also characteristic of ionic radii. There is an important difference, however. For a given element, the radius of the cation is smaller than the atomic radius. This is reasonable because the ns boundary electrons are removed, and the $(n - 1)d$ electrons effectively establish the ion size. In addition, the nuclear charge per electron has increased, and because of this, ions of successively higher charge (for a given element) have successively smaller radii. The dimensions of the titantium atom and its ions may be used to illustrate this point: Ti 1.47 A, Ti^{2+} 0.85A, Ti^{3+} 0.76A, Ti^{4+} 0.68 A.

The experimental ion sizes for the $3d$ elements do not follow the simple trend expected for gaseous species (Figure 1–10). In Figure 1–12 are plotted the effective ionic crystal radii for the M^{2+} ions taken from the MO oxide dimensions. These transitional metal oxides crystallize in the cubic sodium chloride structure, which permits an easy determination of the M^{2+} effective radius. An oxide radius of 1.32 A was used. As can be seen, a curve with

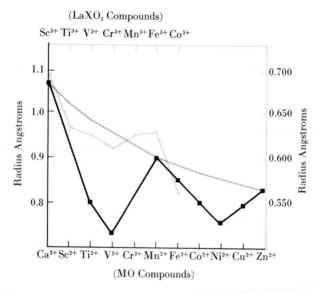

Figure 1–12 **The actual variation of ionic radius of ions of the 3*d* transitional elements versus effective nuclear charge.**

two minima is observed, rather than a linear trend. It should be noted that the radii for the configurations d^0, d^5, and d^{10} lie on a smooth curve.

To rationalize these data it is again necessary to consider the relationship of the *d* orbitals (Figure 1–8) of the metal ion and the symmetry of the oxide ions. In the sodium chloride structure, the metal ions sit at the center of an octahedron of anions. Under these circumstances, the *d* orbitals of the metal ion are split energetically in the weak field of the oxideions. Now correlate the change in ion size with the occupancy of the *d* orbitals (Figure 1–9). The electrons for ions with configurations d^1, d^2, and d^3 occupy the lower energy levels. In these, the metal electrons do not conflict with the ligand electrons, and a decrease in the effective ionic radius occurs because the increase in nuclear charge is the most important parameter. The d^4 and d^5 configurations have the electrons in the d_z^2 and $d_{x^2-y^2}$ orbitals which are directed along the axes also bearing the oxide ligands. The interaction of the metal electrons and ligand electrons results in an effective increase in the metal ion radius. The d^6, d^7, and d^8 configurations have electrons paired in the low energy orbitals, and a decrease in ionic radius is again noted. An expansion in metal ion size occurs with the d^9 and d^{10} configurations where the phenomenon described for the d^4 and d^5 configurations is repeated. A similar trend is noted in the data for the radii of the M^{3+} ions obtained by x-ray studies of $LaXO_3$ compounds where X is a transitional element. An oxide radius of 1.35 A was used here (Figure 1–12).

A consistent set of crystal ionic radii for ions of the $4d$ and $5d$ elements for all possible oxidation states is difficult to assemble. In general, compounds of the elements in a given period and in the same oxidation state have not been prepared. The data that are available are cited in Table 1–3. These data are based on the F^- radius of 1.33 A. The important fact to note is that, starting with zirconium and hafnium in Group IV, the ion sizes of the $4d$ and $5d$ elements in the same group and in the same oxidation state are very similar. Remember that this is a reflection of the contraction within the $4f$ period.

The radii for the M^{3+} ions of the inner-transitional elements are plotted in Figure 1–13 and tabulated in Table A–5 of the Appendix. In the plot, note the linear trend with atomic number.

Table 1–3
Coordination Number 6 Radii for 4d, 5d, and 6d Period Ions*

4d	Y^{3+}	Zr^{4+}	Nb^{5+}	Mo^{4+}	Tc	Ru^{4+}	Rh^{3+}	Pd^{2+}	Ag^{1+}
A	0.92	0.79	0.69	0.70	—	0.67	0.68	0.80	1.26
5d	La^{3+}	Hf^{4+}	Ta^{5+}	W^{4+}	Re^{4+}	Os	Ir^{4+}	Pt^{2+}	Au^{1+}
A	1.14	0.78	0.68	0.70	0.72	—	0.68	0.80	1.37
6d	Ac^{3+}	Th^{4+}							
A	1.18	1.02							

* L. H. Ahrens, *Geochem. and Cosmochem. Acta*, **2**, 155–169 (1952).

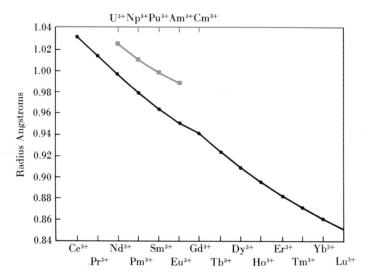

Figure 1–13   Ionic radii of the inner-transitional elements versus effective nuclear charge.

This points up the fact that the f level is buried within an outer electron cloud and that the surrounding ligands have little or no effect on the ion size in contrast to what we have observed for the $3d$ transitional elements. A similar observation is made for the $5f$ elements, although the data are incomplete because of the small quantities of the higher-atomic-numbered elements available for study.

Covalent Radii

Covalent radii result by taking one-half the internuclear distances in covalent molecules in which two atoms of the same element are bonded by a single bond. For instance, in FeS_2 each sulfur atom is surrounded tetrahedrally by three iron atoms and one sulfur atom. The sulfur-sulfur distance is 2.08 A, which when divided in half gives the tetrahedral covalent radius of sulfur. In the same compound, each iron atom is surrounded by six sulfurs at

Table 1–4

Covalent Radii for Atoms of Some of the Transitional Elements*

	Octahedral CN 6			Tetrahedral CN 4	
Element	Fe(II)	Co(II)	Ni(II)	Cu(II)	Zn(II)
Radius A	1.23	1.32	1.39	1.35	1.31
Element	Ru(II)	Rh(III)	Pd(IV)	Ag(I)	Cd(II)
Radius A	1.33	1.32	1.31	1.52	1.48
Element	Os(II)	Ir(III)	Pt(IV)	Au(I)	Hg(II)
Radius A	1.33	1.32	1.31	1.50	1.48

* L. Pauling, *Nature of the Chemical Bond* (3rd ed.; Ithaca, New York: Cornell University Press, 1960), pp. 246–248.

a distance of 2.27 A. When the sulfur distance of 1.04 is subtracted, the difference (1.23) is taken as the octahedral radius for Fe(II). In this manner, a set of radii are determined which are additive.

If covalent bond formation is formally viewed as the donation of a pair of electrons from a ligand to the vacant orbitals of a positive central ion, then the effective covalent radius of that central ion should be larger than the ionic radius of its corresponding free ion. Indeed, the covalent radius ought to be of the same order of magnitude as the atomic radius. Covalent radii for a few of the elements are given in Table 1–4. Compare them with the atomic and ionic radii.

1–6 IONIZATION POTENTIAL

The ionization potential (electron volts) for the atoms and ions of the $3d$, $4d$, and $5d$ transitional elements are plotted in Figure 1–14 and tabulated in Table A–3 of the Appendix. The general trend of increasing values for the ionization potential with increasing atomic number across a period is what one would expect for gaseous atoms and ions of the same charge but decreasing size.

The effect of increasing size down a group is shown by Sc, Y, and La, first members of the $3d$, $4d$, and $5d$ periods, respectively.

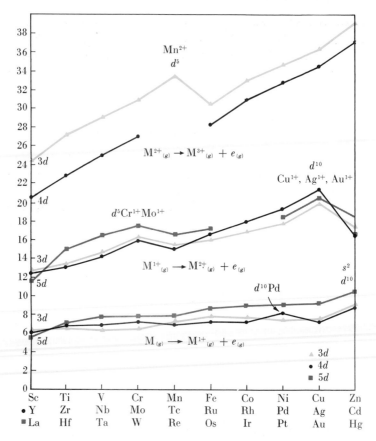

Figure 1–14   The ionization potential of the transitional elements versus effective nuclear charge.

Here the ionization potential decreases within the group, parallelling the increase in size which is consistent with coulombic attraction. It is interesting to note, however, that with few exceptions, the $5d$ elements, starting with element 72, show higher ionization potentials than their $4d$ homologs. This again can be related to the fact that the $4d$ and $5d$ elements have similar radii, with the nuclear charge of the $5d$ species thirty-two units higher than that of the corresponding $4d$ species. The effect of the higher nuclear charge is thus evident. Superimposed on these trends are the preferred stabilities of the d^5, d^{10}, and $d^{10}s^2$ configurations which show maxima in all three ionization plots.

1–7 PARAMAGNETIC PROPERTIES

Figure 1–15 illustrates the Guoy technique for the measurement of magnetic properties of powdered or liquid samples. Experimentally, the magnetic property is determined by hanging, from a balance arm, a cylindrical sample between the poles of an electromagnet. The sample tube and chain are weighed with the

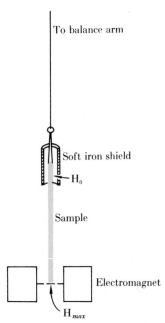

Figure 1–15 The Guoy technique for measurement of magnetic properties.

magnetic field off and then weighed again with the field on. If the field ranges from a maximum at the bottom of the sample to zero at the top of the sample, a resultant downward force on the sample is produced, which is measured by determining the weight necessary to restore the sample to its original position.

The paramagnetic property arises from two sources. One is the magnetic field associated with the spin of an electron; the second is the magnetic field associated with the orbital motion of an electron. The magnitude of the paramagnetic property of an atom or ion depends upon the sum of the orbital and spin contributions for each unpaired electron. Thus, each paramagnetic species has associated with it a resultant magnetic moment, and it is these magnetic moments which are oriented by the magnetic field. Atoms or ions in which all electrons are paired have a net paramagnetic moment of zero.

However, the weight deflection observed in the determination of paramagnetism must be corrected for the presence of a smaller and opposite magnetic property, namely, diamagnetism. This property is separate and distinct from the property due to the orientation of magnetic moments in a magnetic field and is related to the interaction of the electron cloud with the magnetic field. The net effect of this interaction is to move the sample out of the field rather than into the field. The diamagnetic property of matter is usually $1/10$ to $1/100$ that of the paramagnetic property, however, when a large proportion of diamagnetic ions are present, a correction must be made for their contribution to the observed weight change. Tables of diamagnetic corrections are available for this purpose.

A numerical value for the paramagnetic property from the experiment described is obtained by equating the downward force and the restoring force through a proportionally constant $\mathbf{K}$ called the volume susceptibility.

$$g \, \Delta w \, = \, \tfrac{1}{2} H^2 \, A\mathbf{K} \tag{1–1}$$

Here g is the gravitational constant, H is the maximum field strength, Δw the weight necessary to restore the sample to its original position, and A the cross-sectional area of the sample. An absolute determination of $\mathbf{K}$ requires an independent determination of the field strength. In routine determinations, this is not done because all that is needed is a standard with which the weight change per gram of sample can be compared. Compounds for which absolute determinations have been made include $CuSO_4 \cdot 5H_2O$, $FeSO_4(NH_4)_2SO_4$, and $CoHg(SCN)_4$.

The gram susceptibility χ_g is obtained from the volume susceptibility by dividing by the density of the sample, and the molar susceptibility χ_M is obtained by multiplying χ_g by the grams/mole. The molar susceptibility χ_m is related to the number of units of magnetic moment μ_B, the Bohr magneton, by the expression

$$\chi_M = \frac{N^2 \mu_B^2}{3RT} \tag{1-2}$$

$$\mu_B = 2.84\sqrt{\chi_M T} \tag{1-3}$$

where T is the absolute temperature, N Avogadro's number, and R the gas constant. This expression is equivalent to the Curie law which says that χ_M is inversely proportional to the absolute temperature and that the product of the two is a constant.

The number of Bohr magnetons μ_B is in turn related theoretically to the sum of the spin and the orbital contributions J by the equation

$$\mu_B = g\sqrt{J(J+1)} \tag{1-4}$$

The justification for this relationship can be found in more advanced texts, but will not be developed here. The letter g is a constant characteristic of the relative spin and orbital contributions to the magnetic moment. This relationship holds well for the $4f$ elements. The experimental and theoretical values are plotted in Figure 1-16 and, in general, show good agreement. These data emphasize the fact that paramagnetism is not solely a function of the number of unpaired electrons. For instance, Sm^{3+}, with five unpaired electrons, has a smaller magnetic moment than neodymium with three unpaired electrons. Also gadolinium, with seven unpaired electrons, has a magnetic moment of 8.0 μ_B, while holmium with only four unpaired electrons has the maximum moment of 10.4μ_B. This is related to the manner in which the spin and the orbital contributions are added to one another.

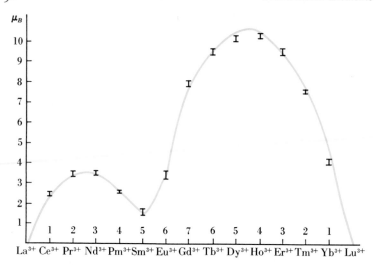

1-16 The magnetic moments of the ions of the 4f elements versus the number of unpaired electrons. The curve is drawn through the theoretical points. I indicates the range of experimental values reported.

On the other hand, for ions of the 3d elements μ_B is simply related to the number of unpaired electrons n by the expression $\mu_B = [n(n + 2)]^{1/2}$. This difference is explained by the fact that for the ions of the transitional elements, the unpaired d electrons are the outermost electrons and thus are subject to the influence of the charge fields of adjacent ions in solids or in solution. The net effect is that the orbital contribution is quenched, and the magnetic moment is in this case simply related to the spin of the unpaired electrons. In this case, $g = 2$ and J is equivalent to $n/2$. Under some circumstances, especially toward the end of the d filling, the orbital contribution is not effectively zero. This accounts for the deviation between the "spin-only" results and the experimental data plotted in Figure 1–17. In contrast, the unpaired f electrons are shielded from the effect of adjacent charge fields by the $5s^2 5p^6$ electrons, and both the spin and orbital contributions must be taken into account.

Care must be taken to differentiate between ferromagnetism, and paramagnetism. Ferromagnetism results from the concerted

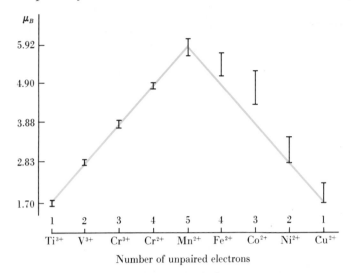

1-17 The magnetic moments of the ions of the 3*d* elements versus the number of unpaired electrons. The curve is drawn through the theoretical points. I indicates the range of experimental values reported.

action of all the ions or atoms in a relatively large volume of a solid to give a magnetic intensity many times greater than that expected from the sum of the individual magnetic moments of each atom. Paramagnetism is much weaker than ferromagnetism, usually being less than one ten-thousandth that of ferromagnetism.

1–8   COLOR OF IONS

It is a simple fact, but one often overlooked, that solutions of ions with rare-gas or pseudo-rare-gas ($s^2p^6d^{10}$) configurations are colorless, while solutions of ions with incomplete d and f electron levels are usually colored. The phenomenon of color is related to the utilization of certain wave lengths of light by the ions in solution to promote electrons to levels of higher energy. In solution, the color we see is the complement of that absorbed in the electron transition. The energy of the transition involved is related to the

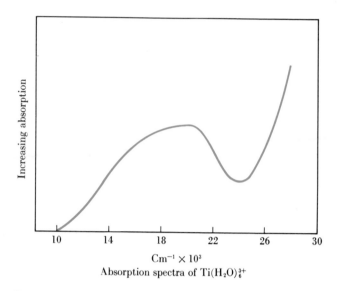

Absorption spectra of $Ti(H_2O)_6^{3+}$

Figure 1-18   Absorption spectra of the $Ti(OH_2)_6^{3+}$ ion in aqueous solution.

wave length of the light by the simple expression $\Delta E = hc/\lambda$, where h is Planck's constant $(6.62 \times 10^{-26}$ erg $\times$ sec), c the velocity of light $(3 \times 10^{10}$ cm/sec), and λ the wave length of the light in centimeters. Because the human eye responds to light only in the limited range of 4,000 to 7,000 Å, we see colors only for the transitions that fall in this range. This is equivalent to 70 to 40 kcal/mole of atoms or ions undergoing the transitions. In the transitional and inner-transitional elements, there are vacant d and f orbitals which are higher in energy than the ground-state energy levels. It is the transition of electrons between these levels which accounts for the visible spectra of these ions. In the ions of elements with complete shells, the energy requirement for promotion of an electron from the ground-state level to a higher level is greater than 70 kcal/mole. These transitions thus have a higher energy requirement and only show up at shorter wave lengths.

The relationship of color to electron configuration may be illustrated with the absorption spectra of the $Ti(OH_2)_6{}^{3+}$ ion (Figure 1–18). The solution shows a maximum absorption at 20,300 cm^{-1} (4,900 Å) and is purple to the eye. Because Ti^{3+} has only one $3d$ electron, the transition responsible for this color must involve this electron. The transition which occurs is simply between the lower and higher d energy levels as split in the field of octahedrally coordinated water (Figure 1–8). The energy difference between the two levels is given by the position of the absorption maximum. In more familiar energy units, 2.03×10^4 cm^{-1} is equal to about 57 kcal (8,068 cm^{-1} equals 23.063 kcal). Thus the absorption spectra can be used to determine the magnitude of Δ. Ions with more than one d electron have a more complicated spectra, and assigning the absorption maxima to the proper electron transitions is more complicated, although the same in principal as the description just presented.

II

The Metals and Their Compounds

2–1   OCCURRENCE

THE SIMILARITY in ion size, along with a common valency of three, accounts for the fact that yttrium, lanthanum, and sometimes scandium are found in nature along with the $4f$ elements. The Lanthanides occur together, the most important ores being $CePO_4$, monazite, and YPO_4, xenotime. The elements of atomic number 65 and up are concentrated in the ore in which yttrium is the most abundant, and the elements of lower atomic number are concentrated in the cerium ore. Element 61, promethium, does not exist in the earth's crust, but the isotope $^{147}_{61}Pm$ is present to the extent of 2.6% in the fission products of $^{235}_{92}U$.

All the $5f$ elements are radioactive. Proactinium is a member of the uranium and thorium decay schemes and therefore occurs in ores of these elements

$$^{235}_{92}U \xrightarrow{\alpha} {}^{231}_{90}Th \xrightarrow{\beta} {}^{231}_{91}Pa \xrightarrow{\alpha} t\tfrac{1}{2} \ 3.4 \times 10^4 \text{ yr}$$

$$^{234}_{90}Th \xrightarrow{\beta} {}^{234}_{91}Pa \xrightarrow{\beta} t\tfrac{1}{2} \ 1.14 \text{ min}$$

34

Uranium is widely distributed in nature, but its most important ore has been U_3O_8. Very small amounts of the transuranium elements are associated with these uranium deposits, but for all practical purposes they are synthetic elements. Element 93 was first produced by Professors McMillan and Abelson of the University of California in 1940. Only element 93 was identified, although since it is a β emitter, element 94 of necessity was the daughter product. However, the very small amount of element 93, coupled with the long half-life of element 94, made the detection of the latter impossible at the time. The reaction originally used (1)* is the one by which plutonium is produced in the nuclear pile; however, the initial identification of element 94 by Professor Glenn Seaborg and his group at the University of California was made on the isotope $^{238}_{92}Pu$ (2). In 1945, the production of elements 95 and 96 as products of the alpha-particle bombardment of uranium and plutonium nuclei in the California cyclotron (3, 4) was revealed. The names americium and curium parallel the names of the corresponding $4f$ elements europium and gadolinium. Americium and europium were named after the continents on which the elements were discovered, and curium and gadolinium were named after the Curie family and J. Gadolin, an early Finnish investigator of the $4f$ elements. By 1950, Seaborg and his group at the University of California Radiation Laboratory had synthesized elements 97 and 98, also by alpha-particle bombardment in the cyclotron (5, 6). The name berklium, of course, is after Berkeley, California, the city in which the elements were produced. This follows the naming of the element 65, terbium, which along with ytterbium, erbium, and yttrium was named after a Swedish town, Ytterby, in which rare earth deposits were located.

Note that the half-lives of the elements become shorter with increasing atomic number. Nuclides with high neutron:proton ratios have longer half-lives than those of the same element with lower ratios. Therefore, equipment was built to permit the acceleration of particles with larger masses in order to introduce more mass into the product nuclei. Thus, californium 246 ($t_{\frac{1}{2}}$ 36

---

* Numbers in parentheses refer to numbers in the left-hand column of Table 2–1.

hr) may be produced by bombardment of uranium 238 with C^{6+} ions. This technique was used (1954) to produce element 98, einsteinium (7). Elements 99 and 100 were also produced by a group from the Argonne National Laboratory by successive neutron capture in a nuclear pile (8, 9). It is interesting to note that in the debris of the first hydrogen device explosion at Eniwetok by the Los Alamos group in 1952, element 100, fermium, as well as element 99, was produced by successive absorption of neutrons.

It should be realized that in many of these reactions, only a

Table 2–1
Methods for the Synthesis of the Transuranium Elements

	Target	Projectile	Product	$t_{\frac{1}{2}}$	Daughter	$t_{\frac{1}{2}}$
1.	$^{238}_{92}U$	$^{1}_{0}n$	$^{239}_{92}U$	β^- 23 min	$^{239}_{93}Np$	β^- 2.3 d
			$^{239}_{93}Np$	β^- 2.3 d	$^{239}_{94}Pu$	α 2.4 $\times$ 10^4 yr
2.	$^{238}_{92}U$	$^{2}_{1}H^{2+}$	$^{238}_{93}Np$	β^- 2.1 d	$^{238}_{94}Pu$	α 86.4 yr
3.	$^{238}_{92}U$	$^{4}_{2}He^{2+}$	$^{241}_{94}Pu$	β^- 13.2 yrs	$^{241}_{95}Am$	α 458 yr
4.	$^{239}_{94}Pu$	$^{4}_{2}He^{2+}$	$^{242}_{96}Cm$	α 162.5 d		
5.	$^{241}_{95}Am$	$^{4}_{2}He^{2+}$	$^{243}_{97}Bk$	ec 4.5 hr		
6.	$^{242}_{96}Cm$	$^{4}_{2}He^{2+}$	$^{245}_{96}Cf$	ec 44 min		
7.	$^{238}_{92}U$	$^{14}_{7}N^{5+}$	$^{246}_{99}Es$	ec 7.3 min		
8.	$^{239}_{94}Pu$	$14\,^{1}_{0}n_Q$	$^{253}_{99}Es$	α 20 d		
9.	$^{239}_{94}Pu$	$15\,^{1}_{0}n$	$^{255}_{100}Fm$	α 22 hr		
10.	$^{253}_{99}Es$	$^{4}_{2}He^{2+}$	$^{256}_{101}Md$	ec 1.5 hr		
11.	$^{246}_{96}Cm$	$^{12}_{6}C^{6+}$	$^{254}_{102}X$	α 3 sec		
12.	$^{252}_{98}Cf$	$^{10}_{5}B^{5+}$	$^{257}_{103}Lw$	α 8 sec		

ec = electron capture; α = helium ion; β^- = electron small number of atoms are produced. In three bombardments, only 40 atoms of einsteinium were produced, and in the production of element 101, only one or two atoms were formed. Mendelevium, element 101, was produced by the California Group in 1955 (10).

The last two elements of the $5f$ period were not isolated and identified themselves but were identified by their radioactive decay products. The originally reported discovery of element 102, by an international team from the Argonne National Laboratory, Harwell and Oslo, could not be repeated by either the California or a Russian Group but has now been synthesized in another reaction by both groups (11). The name, nobelium, given by the initial workers, is presently being reconsidered. The last element of the $5f$ period was synthesized (12) in 1961 by the California Group and named lawrencium after the inventor of the cyclotron, E. O. Lawrence.

Although many scientists contributed to the discovery of these elements, one man, Professor Glenn T. Seaborg, is co-discoverer of all the elements except the first and last. He was co-recipient of the Nobel Prize in Chemistry in 1951 with E. M. McMillan.

The normal transitional elements occur in nature in many different forms, although oxide systems probably predominate. As expected for the valence electron configuration of $(n-1)d^2ns^2$, the normal oxidation state for titanium, zirconium, hafnium, and thorium is four. Although titanium occurs in ores such as rutile, TiO_2, and ilemnite, $FeTiO_3$, and zirconium as zircon, $ZrSiO_4$, and baddlyete, ZrO_2, hafnium has no ore of its own. Hafnium occurs only in the company of zirconium, occurring to the extent of only a few per cent. This emphasizes the similarity of these two elements. It is also interesting to note that hafnium was not discovered until 1923, although zirconium had been known since 1787. Thorium, on the other hand, largely accompanies cerium as the insoluble phosphate ore, monazite.

The elements vanadium, niobium, and tantalum, in accordance with the electron configuration $(n-1)d^3ns^2$, show the oxidation state five in their ores. Whereas vanadium is found in such ores as vanadite, $Pb_2(VO_4)Cl$, and carnotite, $K(UO_2)(VO_4)$, niobium and tantalum occur together in the ores columbite, $Fe(NbO_3)_2$, and tantalite, $Fe(TaO_3)_2$. The Nb:Ta ratio varies with the location of the deposit.

Of the Group Six elements with the valence electron configuration $(n-1)d^4ns^2$, tungsten is the only one to show the oxidation-state six in natural deposits. Chromium occurs largely as chromite, $Fe(CrO_2)_2$, molybdenum as molybdenite, MoS_2, and tungsten as scheelite, $FeWO_4$, and wolframite, $CaWO_4$.

The remaining elements occur either in one of their lower oxidation states or in elemental form. Manganese occurs mainly as pyrolucite, MnO_2, and as the carbonate rhodochrosite, $MnCO_3$. Technetium, on the other hand, does not occur in the earth's crust. It was first identified by the Italian team of Emilo Segrè and C. Perrier, who separated tracer amounts of element 97 from a molybdenum target which had been bombarded in this country in the University of California cyclotron.

$$_{42}^{98}Mo + {}_1^2H \rightarrow {}_{43}^{97}Tc \ (t_{\frac{1}{2}} \ 10^5 \ yr) + 3 \, {}_0^1n$$

Rhenium was not discovered until 1925. Contrary to expectations, it is not found in manganese ores, but rather to the extent of a few hundredths of a per cent along with MoS_2. It is recovered from the roasting operation on molybdenum ores.

The elements of the iron group are found normally as sulfides such as NiSFeS, pentladite; smaltite, CoAsS; pyrites FeS_2; and also as $CoAs_2$, and Fe_2O_3, hematite, Fe_3O_4, magnetite, and $FeCO_3$, siderite.

The inert nature of the remaining elements is shown by the fact that they are found in the native state. The platinum metals also are recovered from Canadian copper sulfide deposits. Copper and silver are found also as the compounds $CuFeS_2$, copper pyrites; Cu_2O, cuprite; $Cu_2(OH)_2CO_3$, malachite; Ag_2S, argentite; and AgCl, horn silver. Silver and gold are also recovered from the anode sludge from the copper purification process.

2–2 SEPARATION METHODS

Although all production processes involve separations for the elimination of impurities, only those processes which involve the separation of two or more transitional elements will be considered here. This situation is encountered with the following pairs and groups of $4d$ and $5d$ elements: zirconium-hafnium, niobium-tantalum, cobalt-nickel, silver-gold, and the platinum metals. In addition, because the $4f$ elements along with lanthanum and yttrium occur together, special methods of separation are required. The same is true of the $5f$ elements because the production of the transuranium elements is not the clean-cut process described by the nuclear equations, but also results in the production of neighboring elements, fission products, and normal daughter decay products.

The $4f$ elements, yttrium and lanthanum, after separation of thorium as the phosphate and cerium as the basic nitrate, are best separated and purified by ion-exchange procedures. The exchangers are water insoluble organic polymers containing $-SO_3H$ groups, the protons of which are exchangeable for other cations. In this procedure, the exchange of M^{3+} cations of the $4f$ elements with the H^+ of the exchanger takes place in a band at the top of a column (Figure 2–1). Then a solution of a

$$3RSO_3H_{(s)} + M^{3+}_{(aq)} \rightarrow (RSO_3)_3M_{(s)} + 3H^+_{(aq)}$$
$$(RSO_3)_3M_{(s)} + H_3 \text{ complexing agent }_{(aq)} \rightarrow 3RSO_3H_{(s)} +$$
$$M \text{ complex }_{(aq)}$$

complexing agent, such as ethylenediaminetetraacetic acid, is added as an eluting agent. The cations are complexed to slightly different extents and are gradually separated into bands containing several elements, as they are absorbed and desorbed while progressing down the column. By proper regulation of the flow, column length, and concentration of reagents, the individual $4f$ elements may be isolated from one another in appropriate fractions. The effectiveness of the separation depends upon the slight differences in the complexing of each element and the affinity of the metal ion for the ion exchanger. The elements come off in reverse order of atomic number (Figure 2–2).

The $5f$ elements have electronic configurations similar to the $4f$ elements and have a tendency to form the oxidation states three or four in solution. The trend in ion size for the same oxidation state of each ion is also similar to that for the $4f$ elements (Figure 1–14). Therefore, a separation process was developed for these elements based on the $4f$ element process. The ion-exchanger technique for

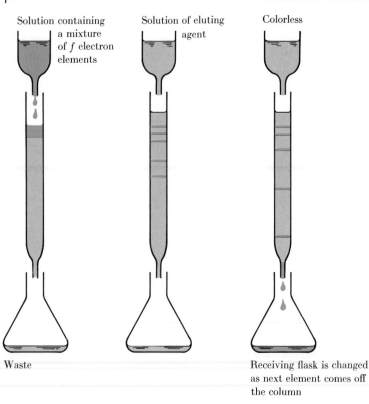

Solution containing
  a mixture
  of f electron
  elements

Solution of eluting
  agent

Colorless

Waste

Receiving flask is changed
as next element comes off
the column

Figure 2–1   Ion exchange separation.

the transuranium elements separation has been developed to such
a fine art that the researchers can predict the drop in which a given
element appears (Figure 2–2).

Many separation processes have been worked out for zirconium and hafnium, but one practical method is the extraction of
an aqueous phase containing the metal ions complexed with thio-
cyanate and sulfate ions, with an organic solvent such as methyl-
ethyl ketone. The hafnium is preferentially extracted into the organic solvent layer, thereby concentrating the zirconium in the
aqueous phase. Still another method involves the preferential re-

duction of zirconium tetrachloride by zirconium metal from a gaseous zirconium-hafnium tetrahalide mixture, thus enriching hafnium in the vapor phase and concentrating zirconium in the solid phase. The advantage of this method is the absence of aque-

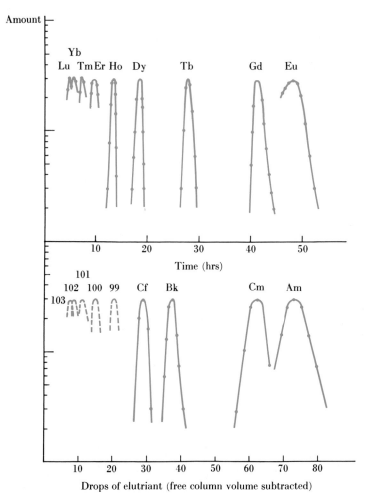

Figure 2–2   Relative elution of homologous actnides and lanthanides.

ous solutions. The separation of these two elements has become important since the discovery that zirconium has a very low cross-section capture for thermal neutrons, while hafnium has a very high cross-section capture for thermal neutrons. In the submarine Nautilus, the uranium fuel slugs were clad with a zirconium-aluminum alloy, while the hafnium was used for the control rods of the nuclear pile.

A solvent extraction method for the separation of niobium and tantalum has been developed also. In this case, the metal ions are complexed in high concentrations of hydrochloric acid and hydrofluoric acid. The tantalum species is preferentially extracted into the organic phase of methylisobutyl ketone.

The fact that nickel forms a volatile carbonyl, $Ni(CO)_4$, under relatively mild conditions permits the separation of cobalt and nickel. Cobalt also forms a volatile carbonyl, but not under the prescribed conditions. The nickel can be easily recovered in pure form by thermal decomposition of the carbonyl at 200°.

The platinum metals are separated on the basis of chemical properties which will not be discussed here. Silver and gold, on the other hand, are separated by a metallurgical process.

2–3   REDUCTION TO THE METAL

The elements are finally prepared for reduction as the purified oxides, or halides. The reduction is accomplished with active metals, carbon, hydrogen, or by electrolysis. Carbon cannot be used if the element forms a stable carbide. The oxide is not used if the metal tends to dissolve in the oxide. Economics very often dictates what reducing agent will be used, although of primary importance are the physical and chemical properties of the products from which the metal must be separated.

Aluminum is used as a reducing agent with the oxides of chromium, vanadium, manganese, cobalt, molybdenum, niobium, and tantalum.

$$Cr_2O_{3(s)} + 2Al_{(l)} \rightarrow Al_2O_{3(l)} + 2Cr_{(l)}$$

The temperature of the reduction is such that the aluminum oxide is molten. If the melting point of the metal is relatively low, it will be molten; the slag and metal may be parted and cast in massive form. In the case of the $4d$ and $5d$ elements, the melting points are high and the metal is recovered as a fine powder.

Titanium, zirconium, hafnium, thorium, the $4f$ elements, and the $5f$ elements are normally reduced from either a fluoride or chloride salt by an active metal.

$$TiCl_{4(l)} + 2Mg_{(s)} \rightarrow Ti_{(s)} + 2MgCl_{2(s)}$$

In this case, the metal chloride product must be separated either by sublimation or aqueous extraction. The resulting metal powder is further purified.

Fused electrolysis of the complex fluorides NbF_7^{2-}, TaF_7^{2-} has been used in the production of these elements. Fused electrolysis has also been used for uranium, and aqueous electrolysis for rhenium and the less active metals.

Presently, rhenium is produced by hydrogen reduction,

$$2NH_4ReO_{4(s)} + 7H_{2(g)} \rightarrow 2NH_{3(g)} + 2Re_{(s)} + 8H_2O_{(g)},$$

while carbon reduction is used for iron, tungsten, and copper.

$$WO_{3(s)} + 3C_{(s)} \rightarrow 3CO_{(g)} + W_{(s)}$$
$$Fe_2O_{3(s)} + 3CO_{(g)} \rightarrow 2Fe_{(l)} + 3CO_{2(g)}$$

Silver and gold may be recovered from their cyanide extracts by reduction with elemental zinc.

$$2Ag(CN)_2^- + Zn \rightarrow 2Ag + Zn^{2+} + 4CN^-$$

The platinum metals may be recovered from any of their compounds by thermal decomposition.

Many elements require further purification or processing. The metals which are recovered as powders may be converted to massive form by melting and casting in vacuo. These procedures must be carried out in the strict absence of oxygen and nitrogen.

Single crystals of high purity may be obtained by thermal decomposition of the metal iodides on a hot tungsten wire. This process is commonly referred to as the Van Arkel process.

$$Zr(crude)_{(s)} + 2I_{2(g)} \rightarrow ZrI_{4(g)} \rightarrow Zr_{(s)} + 2I_{2(g)}$$

Aqueous electrolysis can be used for final purification of chromium, technetium, rhenium, and all the members of Groups Eight and One.

2–4   METHODS OF PREPARATION OF BINARY COMPOUNDS

General Conditions

The conditions of preparation depend upon the energetics of the reactions as well as the rate of reaction. Very often the temperature necessary for a reasonable rate of reaction is such that the product is unstable at that temperature. Under these conditions, the reaction system must be quenched to decrease the rate of the decomposition reaction, or an alternate preparative method must be found. In addition, for most of these metals and compounds, strict absence of moisture and oxygen is required. Thus vacuum-line techniques, inert-gas boxes, and nonaqueous solvent systems are common features of laboratories in which the transitional elements are studied. Many of the reactions involve heterogeneous systems, mainly solid-solid, gas-solid, or liquid-solid. In these cases, the reaction times are usually long because diffusion processes are the rate-controlling steps. Such systems also tend to yield impure products simply because physical contact of the reactants is difficult to achieve. The practical aspect of recovering the product free of reactants and other products must be borne in mind. If the product is more volatile than the other compounds in the system or if a solvent is found in which the product is uniquely soluble, then purification can be achieved simply.

Preparation of the Oxides

Direct Reaction. All of the metals, with the possible exception of gold, react with oxygen to form oxides. The highest possible oxidation state is normally obtained, although this depends upon the thermal stability of the oxide. For instance, rhenium reacts exothermically with oxygen to form Re_2O_7, but manganese yields only MnO_2. The corresponding Mn_2O_7 must be prepared by an indirect method at a lower temperature than that obtained in the direct reaction of the metal with oxygen.

Anhydride formation. This is illustrated by the compounds chromium trioxide and manganese heptoxide, among others. Chromium trioxide is precipitated from solution of a dichromate with concentrated sulfuric acid, while the green oily manganese heptoxide is obtained by the reaction of the same acid on a permanganate.

$$H_2SO_4 + K_2Cr_2O_7 \rightarrow 2CrO_{3(s)} + H_2O + K_2SO_4$$
$$H_2SO_4 + 2KMnO_4 \rightarrow Mn_2O_{7(l)} + H_2O + K_2SO_4$$

Aqueous Oxidation. Silver (II) oxide is made by electrolytic oxidation of a silver (I) salt in aqueous solution with the black insoluble silver (II) oxide being precipitated at the anode. Alternately, the oxidation may be accomplished chemically with potassium peroxydisulfate.

$$Ag^+ + H_2O \rightarrow AgO_{(s)} + \tfrac{1}{2}H_2 + H^+$$
$$2Ag^+ + S_2O_8^{2-} + 2H_2O \rightarrow 2AgO_{(s)} + 4H^+ + 2SO_4^{2-}$$

Anhydrous Oxidation. Occasionally more strenuous conditions are required. For example, the normal atmospheric oxidation products of praseodymium, terbium, and curium are Pr_6O_{11}, Tb_4O_7, and Cm_2O_3. The dioxides are prepared from these oxides by reaction with atomic oxygen, ozone, or molecular oxygen under high pressure.

$$Pr_6O_{11(s)} + (O)_{(g)} \rightarrow 6PrO_{2(s)}$$
$$Cm_2O_{3(s)} + \tfrac{1}{3}O_{3(g)} \rightarrow 2CmO_{2(s)}$$

Dehydration. It is sometimes convenient to simply dehydrate water-insoluble hydroxides or hydrated oxides as illustrated by nickel (II) hydroxide and hydrated zirconium oxide.

$$Ni(OH)_{2(s)} \rightarrow NiO_{(s)} + H_2O_{(g)}$$
$$ZrO_2 \cdot x\,H_2O_{(s)} \rightarrow ZrO_{2(s)} + x\,H_2O_{(g)}$$

Thermal Decomposition of Salt with Oxyanion. On the other hand, there may be oxyanion salts or sulfides which can be precipitated or crystallized in a form which is easier to recover from solution than the voluminous hydroxides. These can be decomposed to give the oxide and gaseous products as illustrated by the following equations.

$$EuCO_{3(s)} \rightarrow EuO_{(s)} + CO_{2(g)}$$
$$Gd_2(C_2O_4)_{3(s)} \rightarrow Gd_2O_{3(s)} + 3CO_{2(g)} + 3CO_{(g)}$$
$$UO_2(NO_3)_{2(s)} \rightarrow UO_{3(s)} + 2NO_{2(g)} + \tfrac{1}{2}O_{2(g)}$$
$$2MoS_{2(s)} + 7O_{2(g)} \rightarrow 2MoO_{3(s)} + 4SO_{2(g)}$$

Thermal Decomposition and Reduction. Oxides of lower oxidation state may be prepared by thermal decomposition, disproportionation, reduction of a higher oxide with hydrogen, carbon (under conditions where no carbide is formed), carbon monoxide, or the metal itself. The temperature of the reaction is very often critical, for instance, whereas hydrogen reduction of vanadium pentoxide at 600° yields V_2O_3, at 1700° it yields non-stoichiometric $VO_{0.94-1.12}$. Examples of these reactions are given in the following equations.

$$2CrO_{3(s)} \rightarrow Cr_2O_{3(s)} + \tfrac{3}{2}O_{2(g)}$$
$$Nb_2O_{5(s)} + H_{2(g)} \rightarrow 2NbO_{2(s)} + H_2O_{(g)}$$
$$Ta_2O_{5(s)} + C_{(s)} \rightarrow 2TaO_{2(s)} + CO_{(g)}$$
$$UO_{3(s)} + CO_{(g)} \rightarrow UO_{2(s)} + CO_{2(g)}$$
$$3Tc_2O_{7(g)} + Tc_{(s)} \rightarrow 7TcO_{3(s)}$$
$$3ReO_{3(s)} \rightarrow Re_2O_{7(g)} + ReO_{2(s)}$$

Preparation of the Halides

Direct Reaction. The simplest possible synthetic method is the direct reaction of the metal and a halogen. It is appropriate when the physical properties of the product are sufficiently different from the halogen to allow efficient separation of the two. Like the oxide syntheses, the halogen-metal reactions are usually quite exothermic and the oxidation state obtained is that which is compatible with the temperature attained and the thermal stability of the halide. The thermal stabilities of the halides for a given oxidation state are known to increase in the order, $I < Br < Cl < F$. Thus, fluorine very frequently brings out an oxidation state that is not obtained with the other halogens, as evidenced by the formation of VF_5, ReF_7, CrF_6, MoF_6, PtF_6, NpF_6, PuF_6, CmF_4, and CeF_4.

However, MnF_7, RuF_8, and OsF_8 are not known, although oxides of the elements in these oxidation states are known. On the other hand, the highest oxidation-state chlorides of these elements are: VCl_4, $ReCl_6$, $CrCl_3$, $MoCl_5$, $PtCl_4$, $NpCl_4$, $PuCl_3$, $CmCl_3$, and $CeCl_3$.

It is well to realize that chemical equations do not convey sufficient information to describe a synthesis, so additional information about conditions must be prescribed. Thus, the hexafluoride of chromium is obtained under a fluorine pressure of 350 atmospheres at 400° in the presence of a manganese catalyst, followed by quenching the reaction vessel to liquid air temperatures. The yellow CrF_6 must be preserved at low temperatures for it is observed to decompose rapidly at $-100°$ to bright red CrF_5. In another case, the reaction of fluorine on rhenium metal at 250 mm pressure and 300 to 400°, yields pale yellow ReF_7, while the same reactants at 125° in the presence of excess metal yield yellow ReF_6.

Halogen Exchange. This has been used especially for fluorine compounds, because elemental fluorine has been readily available only in relatively recent years. Anhydrous hydrogen fluoride, silver (II) fluoride and antimony trifluoride are examples of compounds used in the exchange reaction. For example, zirconium tetrachloride suspended in an inert liquid is converted to the tetrafluoride with anhydrous hydrogen fluoride, with the evolution of volatile hydrogen chloride.

$$4HF_{(g)} + ZrCl_{4(s)} \rightarrow ZrF_{4(s)} + 4HCl_{(g)}$$

Dehydration. Normally in the preparation of anhydrous compounds, aqueous solutions are avoided, although there are instances in which an anhydrous salt can be successfully obtained. The difficulty arises from the fact that hydrates, when heated, normally decompose to a hydrohalogen and an oxysalt.

$$LaCl_3 \cdot 6H_2O_{(s)} \rightarrow LaOCl_{(s)} + 2HCl_{(g)} + 5H_2O_{(g)}$$

This reaction can be repressed by the presence of added hydrohalogen gas, under which conditions the dehydration may be accomplished.

$$LaCl_3 \cdot 6H_2O_{(s)} \xrightarrow{HCl} LaCl_{3(s)} + 6H_2O_{(g)}$$

Some hydrates may be dehydrated by refluxing in a hydrolyzable liquid such as $SOCl_2$. Anhydrous thorium (IV), cobalt (II), nickel (II), copper (II), chromium (III), and iron (III) chloride all have been successfully prepared by this method.

$$CrCl_3 \cdot 6H_2O_{(s)} + 6SOCl_{2(l)} \rightarrow CrCl_{3(s)} + 12HCl_{(g)} + 6SO_{2(g)}$$

Decomposition of Ternary Salts. Certain ternary halide salts can be isolated from aqueous solution as anhydrous salts. These, when heated, yield the anhydrous halide and the volatile ammonium or pyridinium halide. For example,

$$(NH_4)_2HfF_{6(s)} \rightarrow HfF_{4(s)} + 2NH_4F_{(g)}$$
$$(pyH)_2ZrCl_{6(s)} \rightarrow ZrCl_{4(s)} + 2pyHCl_{(g)}$$

Precipitation Reactions. The chlorides, bromides, and iodides of silver (I), and copper (I) are insoluble in water and may be recovered as anhydrous compounds by dehydration in vacuo at relatively low temperature. Because copper (I) ions are unstable in aqueous solution, copper (II) salts are used as starting materials, and a reducing agent must be supplied. For instance, copper (I) chloride and bromide may be prepared using sulfite ion as the reducing agent.

$$2Cu^{2+} + 2Cl^- + SO_3^{2-} + H_2O \rightarrow 2CuCl_{(s)} + SO_4^{2-} + 2H^+$$

The iodide is prepared using the iodide ion itself as the reducing agent. The fluorides of the Group III elements and $4f$ and $5f$ elements in the oxidation states III and IV are insoluble in water and may be obtained free of oxysalts by removing the last traces of water in an atmosphere of hydrogen fluoride.

Halogenation of Oxide. Except for fluorine, the reaction of halogen and an oxide usually results in the formation of an oxy-compound. Thus, chlorine reacts with vanadium pentoxide to form vanadium oxychloride.

$$3Cl_{2(g)} + V_2O_{5(s)} \rightarrow 2VOCl_{3(g)} + \tfrac{3}{2}O_{2(g)}$$

In general, oxides may be used as starting materials as long as some oxygen carrier is present. A variety of elements and compounds have been used for this purpose, including elemental carbon, chlorinated hydrocarbons, and sulfur monochloride. For example, anhydrous chlorides and bromides may be prepared by passing the halogen over a heated mixture of carbon and the oxide.

$$TiO_{2(s)} + 2C_{(s)} + 2Br_{2(g)} \xrightarrow{300°} TiBr_{4(s)} + 2CO_{(g)}$$

Chlorinations may be improved by using carbon tetrachloride or a chlorinated hydrocarbon such as hexchlorobutadiene and an oxide in a bomb under pressure.

$$WO_{3(s)} + 3CCl_{4(l)} \xrightarrow{400°} WCl_{6(s)} + 3COCl_{2(g)}$$

The oxygen carrying product, phosgene, dissolves in the excess liquid, and care must be taken upon opening to provide a means of escape for this very toxic gas. This method has been used to produce high purity $FeCl_3$, $ReCl_5$, $MoCl_5$, WCl_6, $ZrCl_4$, $HfCl_4$, UCl_4, $TaCl_5$, and $NbCl_5$. Fluorine shows less tendency to form oxysalts, especially if the fluoride is one which is insoluble in water. In such cases, an anhydrous fluoride can be recovered from the reaction of anhydrous hydrogen fluoride and an oxide. Uranium tetrafluoride can be prepared in this manner.

$$UO_{2(s)} + 4HF_{(g)} \rightarrow UF_{4(s)} + 2H_2O_{(g)}$$

This is of considerable practical importance in the production of uranium hexafluoride, because only one mole of elemental fluorine will then be required for the production of one mole of uranium hexafluoride, rather than the three moles required when starting from the metal. Uranium hexafluoride is used in the gaseous diffusion process for the separation of uranium 235 from uranium 238.

Reduction Reactions. Halides of lower and intermediate oxidation states may be prepared by reduction of halides of the higher oxidation states. The reducing agent used varies with the chemical properties of the compound. Thus, elemental hydrogen reduces titanium (IV) chloride to titanium (III) chloride in the presence of a red hot tungsten wire:

$$TiCl_{4(g)} + \tfrac{1}{2}H_{2(g)} \rightarrow TiCl_{3(s)} + HCl_{(g)}$$

It will also reduce vanadium (III), chromium (III), and europium (III) chlorides to the dihalides at temperatures of 500–700°. However, it will not reduce the zirconium, hafnium, or thorium (IV) halides. For this purpose, atomic hydrogen produced in a glow discharge is suitable.

$$ZrCl_{4(g)} + H_{(g)} \rightarrow ZrCl_{3(s)} + HCl_{(g)}$$

Active metals such as aluminum may be used as reducing agents. However, unless there is a suitable method for the separation of reaction products, the use of a second metal complicates the system. To overcome this, the element itself may be used as the reducing agent.

$$3ZrBr_{4(g)} + Zr_{(s)} \xrightarrow[500°]{} 4ZrBr_{3(s)}$$

If the product is not volatile, it deposits on the surface of the metal, and the rate of reaction is controlled by the rate at which the tetrahalide diffuses through the trihalide layer. It sometimes is possible to remove the product layer from the reducing agent by mechanical abrasion.

Disproportionation. Disproportionation reactions provide a route to the lower oxidation states but, at the same time, make the synthesis of the intermediate state more difficult. Thus tungsten (IV) chloride is unstable at 475° with respect to tungsten (II) chloride and tungsten (V) chloride.

$$3WCl_{4(s)} \xrightarrow{475°} WCl_{2(s)} + 2WCl_{5(g)}$$

Because the higher state is more volatile than the lower state, a purification may be effected. However, the dihalide will normally show the same kind of reaction.

$$5WCl_{2(s)} \xrightarrow[627°]{} 2WCl_{5(g)} + 3W_{(s)}$$

Thus, the success of the procedure depends upon the difference in these two temperatures. If they are reasonably far apart, a pure product may be isolated; if they are close together, the preparation of a pure product is very difficult by this procedure.

2–5 CHEMICAL PROPERTIES OF BINARY COMPOUNDS

Thermal Decomposition

The thermal stability of a compound may be measured by the heat of formation, $\Delta H°$ of the compound from its elements.

$$m\,M_{(s)} + \frac{n}{2}\,X_{2(g)} \rightarrow M_mX_{n(s)} + \text{heat of formation} \quad (2\text{-}1)$$

Care must be taken to identify the state of the reactants and products. The state in which the elements and compounds exist at 25° are normally taken as the standard states. One atmosphere pressure is the standard state for gases. The heats are expressed in kcal/mole of product. Negative heats refer to the loss of energy by the system; the larger the negative heat of formation, the more stable the compound is with respect to decomposition to the elements. Heats of formation can only be easily compared for compounds with the same stoichiometry, although large differences in heats of formation reflect substantial differences in stability regardless of the compounds being compared.

Thermochemical equations are additive, and so equation (2-1) can be broken down into a series of hypothetical steps, each with its own energy requirements. Such a set of equations allows an understanding of why one compound is more stable than another. The steps are set down as follows:

Process	Equation	Sign
Sublimation	$m\,M_{(s)} \rightarrow m\,M_{(g)}$	endothermic +
Ionization	$m\,M_{(g)} \rightarrow m\,M_{(g)}^{n+} + nm\,e$	endothermic +
Dissociation	$\dfrac{n}{2}\,X_{2(g)} \rightarrow n\,X_{(g)}$	endothermic +
Electron Affinity	$n\,X_{(g)} + nm\,e \rightarrow n\,X_{(g)}^{m-}$	exothermic 1e − endothermic 2e +
Crystal Lattice Energy	$n\,M_{(g)}^{n+} + n\,X_{(g)}^{m} \rightarrow M_mX_{n(s)}$	exothermic −
Heat of Formation	$m\,M_{(s)} + n/2\,X_{2(g)} \rightarrow M_mX_{n(s)}$	

This can be summarized as follows:

Heat of formation = Sublimation Energy + Ionization Potential + $n/2$ Dissociation Energy + Electron Affinity + Crystal Lattice Energy

Care must be taken to use the appropriate sign for each process. This type of calculation is referred to as the Born-Haber Cycle.

One component of this set may be calculated if all other components are known. Although this type of calculation was originally used to arrive at crystal lattice energies or electron affinities, it can also be used to estimate heats of formation. The parameters may all be arrived at experimentally except for the crystal lattice energy, which now can be calculated accurately for ionic solids of known crystal structure. As the bonding becomes more covalent, the reliability of the calculation decreases, although a value for an equivalent term can be calculated if an experimental heat of formation is available. The crystal lattice energy U^0 is proportional to the product of the charge on the ions $Ze^+ \cdot Ze^-$, and inversely proportional to the distance between the nuclei $U^0 \propto (Ze^+ \cdot Ze^-)/r$.

The crystal lattice energy for metal halides of a given metal and structure decreases $F > Cl > Br > I$, because the ionic radii increase in this direction. Because the crystal lattice energy is usually a rather large negative term, it can be the dominant factor in determining the magnitude of the heat of formation. The other parameters in this case are the electron affinity, which increases $I < Br < F < Cl$, and the dissociation energy, which increases in the order $I \sim F < Br < Cl$. The electron affinity is exothermic for the addition of one electron, while the dissociation energy is endothermic; both are smaller than the crystal lattice energy. The net effect is that the thermal stabilities of the halides for a given metal increase in the order $I < Br < Cl < F$. This is illustrated by the data in Table 2–2, in which the known halides are listed along with those heats of formation which are available.

When comparing heats of formation of compounds with the same anion but different metals, the steps of significance are the crystal lattice energy, ionization potential, and sublimation energy. The dissociation energy and the electron affinity need not be considered, because these terms are common to the secycles. In general, for the same anion, the heats of formation decrease along a period and increase down a group. The platinum metals and the copper group are exceptions to this.

The halides and oxides of the transitional elements have such negative heats of formation that they cannot be decomposed to the elements at ordinary laboratory temperatures. Exceptions to this are compounds of the platinum metals, silver, and gold. The instability of silver oxide, Ag_2O, compared to sodium oxide, Na_2O, can be related to the higher positive values of the sublimation energy and ionization potential for silver, coupled with a larger negative value for the crystal lattice energy for sodium oxide. The net result is that silver oxide is 92 kcal/mole less stable than sodium oxide.

Other thermal reactions are thermal decompositions to a lower oxidation state and disproportionation. Thermal decomposition to a lower oxidation state is really the only reaction for a compound in which the metal is in its highest oxidation state.

$$MX_n \rightarrow MX_{n-1} + \tfrac{1}{2}X_2 \qquad (2\text{-}2)$$

Because this reaction is the difference of reactions 2–3 and 2–4,

$$M + \frac{n-1}{2} X_2 \rightarrow MX_{n-1} \qquad (2\text{-}3)$$

$$M + \frac{n}{2} X_2 \rightarrow MX_n \qquad (2\text{-}4)$$

the heat of reaction for the net equation (2–2) can be obtained by subtracting the heat of formation of the reactant species MX_n from the heat of formation for the product species MX_{n-1}. The magnitude and sign of the heat of reaction can be used as a fair measure of whether or not the reaction will go. A large positive value indicates that the reaction is unlikely to go, while a large negative value indicates that the reaction probably will go. For example

$$VF_4 \rightarrow VF_3 + \tfrac{1}{2}F_2 \qquad \Delta H^\circ{}_r = \Delta H^\circ{}_{VF_3} - \Delta H^\circ{}_{VF_4}$$
$$= -285 - (-325)$$
$$= 40 \text{ kcal/mole}$$
$$CrI_3 \rightarrow CrI_2 + \tfrac{1}{2}I_2 \qquad \Delta H^\circ{}_r = \Delta H^\circ{}_{CrI_2} - \Delta H^\circ{}_{CrI_3}$$
$$= -58 - (-47.8)$$
$$= -10.2 \text{ kcal/mole}$$

In general, thermal decomposition to a lower oxidation state is most favorable for iodides and least favorable for fluorides. This accounts for the lack of iodides (Table 2–2), especially among the higher oxidation states.

Table 2-2

Standard Heats of Formation (−kcal/mole) of the Transitional Element Binary Halides

	F⁻	Cl⁻	Br⁻	I⁻
3d ScX₃	(367)	221	190.4	(149)
TiX₄	393.6	194.9	(170)	(131)
TiX₃	335.2	172.4	(143)	(102)
TiX₂	218	123.5	(102)	(76)
VX₅	(335)			
VX₄	(325)	(141)	(129)	
VX₃	(285)	(137)	(120)	—
VX₂	(180)	(102)	(104)	(77)
CrX₆	—			
CrX₅	—			
CrX₄	266			
CrX₃	(266)	132	(102)	47.8
CrX₂	182	97.3	(81)	(58)
MnX₃	(238)			
MnX₂	190	115.2	96	72
FeX₃	235	95.7	(76)	
FeX₂	168	81.9	60	30
CoX₃	(190)			
CoX₂	158	74	58	36
NiX₂	158	73	59	38
CuX₂	128	53.4	41.3	
CuX	60	32.6	29.1	16.4

	F⁻	Cl⁻	Br⁻	I⁻
RhX₃	143.6	40.1	50	40
RhX₂	100.2	—	30	15
4d PdX₃	99.6			
PdX₂	101.9	33.2	32	25
AgX₂	84.5			
AgX	48.7	30.3	27.4	14.9
5d LaX₃	421	264	(233)	189
HfX₄	435	237	(225)	(175)
HfX₃		(220)		
HfX₂		(150)		
TaX₅	—	—		
TaX₄				
TaX₃				
WX₆	422	163.1		
WX₅		137	(60)	
WX₄		121	(50)	(30)
WX₃				
WX₂		60		
ReX₇	—			
ReX₆	275	378	(26)	16
ReX₅	—			
ReX₄	—			

Table 2–2 (Continued)

4d	F⁻	Cl⁻	Br⁻	I⁻
YX_3	(397)	235	(208)	165
ZrX_4	456.8	234.7	181.6	(160)
ZrX_3	(330)	(190)	(185)	(150)
ZrX_2	(230)	(132)	(127)	(105)
NbX_5	—	—	—	—
NbX_4	—	—	—	—
NbX_3	—	—	—	—
MoX_6	—	90.8	(60)	(48)
MoX_5	—	(79)	(51)	—
MoX_4	—	—	(36)	(27)
MoX_3	—	(44)	—	—
MoX_2	—	—	—	—
TcX_6	—	—	—	—
TcX_5	—	—	—	—
TcX_4	—	—	—	—
RuX_6	—	—	—	—
RuX_5	—	—	—	—
RuX_4	—	—	—	—
RuX_3	—	31.4	(35)	—
RhX_4	—	—	—	—

5d	F⁻	Cl⁻	Br⁻	I⁻
ReX_3	—	—	—	—
OsX_6	—	—	—	—
OsX_5	—	—	—	—
OsX_4	—	—	—	—
OsX_3	—	—	—	—
OsX_2	—	23.1	24	17
IrX_6	—	—	—	—
IrX_4	—	—	—	—
IrX_3	—	34.5	(40)	(36)
IrX_2	—	23.8	27	20
PtX_6	—	—	—	—
PtX_5	—	—	—	—
PtX_4	—	—	47	40
PtX_3	—	43	35	31
PtX_2	—	29	23	19
AuX_3	—	28	—	—
AuX	—	8	—	7.2
6d AcX_3	(420)	(260)	(231)	(192)
ThX_4	(477)	284.5	245	191
ThX_3	—	—	—	—

Table 2-2 (Continued)

	F⁻	Cl⁻	Br⁻	I⁻		F⁻	Cl⁻	Br⁻	I⁻
4f CeX₄	—				5f UX₅	485.2	262.1		
CeX₃	416	260	228	185	UX₄	443	251.2	196.6	127
PrX₃	(413)	(258)	(225)	184	UX₃	357	213	170.1	114.7
SmX₃	405	248	216	174	NpX₆	463			
SmX₂	(290)	(205)	(182)	(155)	NpX₄	428	237	183	
GdX₃	404	245	214	170	NpX₃	360	216	174	120
EuX₃	(391)	(233)	(202)	(159)	PuX₆	392			
EuX₂	(300)	(210)	(187)	(160)	PuX₄	424			
TbX₄	—				PuX₃	374.6	230.1	187.8	133
YbX₃	376	(214)	(185)	(143)	AmX₄	400			
YbX₂	(280)	(180)	(157)	(135)	AmX₃	393	251.3		
LuX₃	(392)	228	(200)	155	CmX₄	—			
5f PaX₅	—	—	—	—	CmX₃	—			
UX₆	517	272.4							

— Means compound is known but no data are available.

The Group III elements show only the oxidation state three both as halides and oxides, while the remaining elements show oxidation states differing by units of one. Among the $3d$ elements, chromium is the only one to show the oxidation state six, while chromium and vanadium have the oxidation state five. The oxidadation state four is shown only by titanium, vanadium, and chromium. The stability of the oxidation state three with respect to decomposition to the oxidation state two decreases across a period. Down a group, the stability of the higher oxidation state with respect to decomposition to a lower oxidation state increases. Thus, manganese only forms MnF_3, while technetium and rhenium form TcF_6 and ReF_7, respectively. The same observation is made for the oxides; for example, RuO_4 and OsO_4 are both known, but the corresponding iron compound is not.

The oxidation state three is the predominate state for the $4f$ halides and oxides. Only cerium, terbium, and praseodymium show the oxidation state four, although praseodymium tetrafluoride has not yet been prepared. The oxidation state two is well established for samarium, europium, and ytterbium, although studies on the reaction of the $4f$ metals with the fused metal halides show evidence for the oxidation state two for cerium, neodymium, and praseodymium as well. It is interesting to note that $Ce(IV)$ is isoelectronic with the rare gas xenon, europium (II), and terbium (IV) with the half-filled shell, $4f^7$, and ytterbium (II) with the complete $4f^{14}$ configuration.

Like the $4f$ elements, the $5f$ elements have a valence electron configuration of $5f^n\ 6d^1\ 7s^2$ and would be expected to have a common valency of three. However, the energy requirements for the removal of additional electrons is much lower for the $5f$ electrons than the $4f$ electrons, and oxidation states higher than three are common. The halides of the $5f$ elements show a larger number of compounds than do the oxides (Table 2–3). Although neptunium and plutonium do not have an oxide corresponding to UO_3, they do have a MF_6 compound. Uranium is the only one of these elements for which the oxidation state five has been confirmed in a solid binary compound. Note the tendency toward the stability of the oxidation state three as the f orbitals approach the point of half-filling in curium (III).

Table 2-3
Standard Heats of Formation (−kcals/mole) of Transitional Element Oxides

3d		4d		5d		6d	
Sc_2O_3	(411)	Y_2O_3	420	La_2O_3	428.6	Ac_2O_3	444
TiO_2	225.5	ZrO_2	261.5	HfO_2	266.1	ThO_2	293.2
Ti_2O_3	362.9						
TiO	123.9						
						5f	
V_2O_5	373	Nb_2O_5	455.2	Ta_2O_5	488.9	Pa_2O_5	—
VO_2	171	NbO_2	246.0	TaO_2	—		
V_2O_3	296						
VO	100	NbO	—				
CrO_3	137.7	MoO_3	180.3	WO_3	201.5	UO_3	291.6
Cr_2O_3	272.7	$MoO_{2.75}$	167.5	$WO_{2.72}$	181.5	U_3O_8	853.5
CrO_2	142.5	MoO_2	132.5	WO_2	140.9	UO_2	259.2
Mn_2O_7	—	Tc_2O_7	266.0	Re_2O_7	297	NpO_2	246
		TcO_3	129.0	ReO_3	147	PuO_2	—
MnO_2	124.5	TcO_2	103.4	ReO_2	103.4	Pu_2O_3	—
Mn_3O_4	331.4					AmO_2	—
Mn_2O_3	229.2					Am_2O_3	—
MnO	92.1					CmO_2	—
		RuO_4	52	OsO_4	93	Cm_2O_3	—
		RuO_2	56.5	OsO_2	62	*4f*	
						CeO_2	—
Fe_2O_3	196.8					Ce_2O_3	435
Fe_3O_4	267.8					PrO_2	230.5
FeO	63.8					Pr_6O_{11}	—
Co_3O_4	204	Rh_2O_3	68.5	IrO_2	40	Pr_2O_3	—
CoO	57	RhO	23.9			Sm_2O_3	430
NiO	57.3	PdO	22.9	PtO	(17)	TbO_2	—
Cu_2O	40.4	Ag_2O	7.3	Au_2O	d	Tb_4O_7	—
CuO	37.6	AgO	—	Au_2O_3	0.8	Tb_2O_3	—

Disproportionation requires a stable higher oxidation state as well as a stable lower oxidation state. For example,

$$2VF_4 \rightarrow VF_5 + VF_3 \qquad \Delta H_r = \Delta H^0{}_{VF_5} + \Delta H^0{}_{VF_3} - 2\Delta H^0{}_{VF_4}$$
$$= -335 \; -285 \; -(2)(-325)$$
$$= +30 \; kcal/mole$$

Although vanadium tetrafluoride is stable with respect to disproportionation at room temperature, it will decompose according to the above equation at elevated temperatures. This is in contrast to VCl_4 whose only route for decomposition is to VCl_3.

Hydrolysis and Oxygenation

The anhydrous halides, especially those of elements in high oxidation states, react readily with water and in some cases oxygen to form oxycations, oxyanions, or neutral volatile molecules. The cationic species are found especially among the compounds of the Group III, IV, $4f$, and $5f$ elements. Examples of these compounds are $Zr_4(OH)_8Cl_8 \cdot 16H_2O$, $ThOCl_2$, $LaOCl$, and UO_2Cl_2. Examples of the neutral volatile molecules are found mainly among the compounds of the elements of Groups V through VII, and some of the Group VIII elements. Examples of these compounds are $VOCl_3$, CrO_2F_2, $MoOF_4$, MoO_2Cl_2, $WOCl_4$, WO_2Cl_2, TcO_3Cl, $ReOF_5$, $Ru_2Cl_{10}O$, and ReO_2F_2 among others. Anionic species are found largely among the platinum metals and are typified by $RuO_2Cl_4{}^{2-}$, $OsO_4F_2{}^{2-}$, and $OsO_3X_2{}^{2-}$.

Addition Compound Formation

Most of the halides are capable of reacting with molecules which are electron pair donors to form addition compounds. In the Lewis acid-base sense, the halides are Lewis acids. Reactions such as represented in the following equations are plentiful. The bases may be inorganic or organic species. The absence of water from the system is required.

$$TiCl_4 + 2POCl_3 \rightarrow TiCl_4 \cdot 2POCl_3$$
$$TaCl_4 + 2 \; pyridine \rightarrow TaCl_4 \cdot 2 \; pyridine$$

Normally the 2:1 compounds are thermally unstable and decompose to 1:1 compounds upon heating.

Ternary Compound Formation

Ternary compounds may result from the reaction of a binary compound in a melt or in some other nonaqueous solvent. For instance,

$$\text{ReF}_6 + 2\text{KF} \xrightarrow[\text{SO}_2]{} \text{K}_2\text{ReF}_8$$

$$6\text{NH}_4\text{HF}_{2(s)} + \text{V}_2\text{O}_{3(s)} \xrightarrow{250^\circ} 2(\text{NH}_4)_3\text{VF}_{6(s)} + 3\text{H}_2\text{O}_{(g)}$$

$$2\text{NaCl} + \text{ZrCl}_4 \xrightarrow{400^\circ} \text{Na}_2\text{ZrCl}_6$$

The oxides, especially, form a very large number of ternary compounds from melts. Compounds which have the general formula $\text{M}^{\text{II}}\text{Al}_2\text{O}_4$ or $\text{M}^{\text{IV}}\text{Mg}_2\text{O}_4$ are called spinels, and those of the formula $\text{M}^{\text{II}}\text{M}^{\text{IV}}\text{O}_3$, $\text{M}^{\text{III}}\text{M}^{\text{III}}\text{O}_3$, or $\text{M}^{\text{I}}\text{M}^{\text{V}}\text{O}_3$ are called perovskites. The spinels are typified by compounds such as FeAl_2O_4, CoAl_2O_4, and TiMg_2O_4, and the perovskites by CaTiO_3, LaAlO_3, KMgF_3, and NaWO_3. Actually, in these instances, the $\text{Al}_2\text{O}_4{}^{2-}$ and $\text{TiO}_3{}^{2-}$ ions do not exist as discrete units. The structures will be discussed in Chapter 3.

Very frequently an oxidation state which is not stable in a simple binary compound will be stabilized in a solid ternary compound. There are a large number of ternary fluorides which illustrate this; some are Ca_2CoF_6, KAgF_4, BaNiF_5, NaMnF_5, Cs_3NdF_7, and K_2CrF_6. These are prepared by the reaction of elemental fluorine on a solid mixture of an alkali fluoride and a transitional element halide.

$$\tfrac{3}{2}\text{F}_{2(g)} + 3\text{KF}_{(s)} + \text{CuCl}_{2(s)} \rightarrow \text{K}_3\text{CuF}_{6(s)} + \text{Cl}_{2(g)}$$

Some ternary compounds can be recovered from aqueous solution. In many of these cases, structural studies have shown that the discrete complex ions do exist as such in the solid state. Thus, the compounds $(\text{NH}_4)_2\text{ZrF}_6$ and K_2TaF_7 can be recovered from fluoride solutions. In these solids, the $\text{ZrF}_6{}^{2-}$ and $\text{TaF}_7{}^{2-}$ ions occupy lattice positions. Examples of other ternary compounds which may be recovered from aqueous solution are given in the following equations.

$$KCl + KTcO_4 + 8HCl \rightarrow K_2TcCl_6 + 4H_2O + \tfrac{3}{2}Cl_2$$
$$2KCl + PtCl_2 \rightarrow K_2PtCl_4$$
$$OsO_4 + 4FeCl_2 + 8HCl + 2NH_4Cl \rightarrow (NH_4)_2(OsCl_6) +$$
$$4FeCl_3 + 4H_2O$$

III

The Structure of the Metals and Their Compounds

THE METALS, their alloys, binary and ternary compounds can be systematized structurally by considering the solids in terms of the closest packing of atoms and ions. The structural features of the solid state can in turn be related to the observed physical properties. These features of the solid-state chemistry are developed in the succeeding sections of this chapter. It is first necessary to develop some of the principles upon which structures in general are based.

3–1 THE CLOSE PACKING OF SPHERES

Let us start by considering how spheres pack together. Place a group of spheres in a layer and squeeze them together so that all the spheres are in contact with one another. It is apparent that six spheres can be arranged symmetrically in the form of a hexagon with a seventh in the center (Figure 3–1). This is shown in expanded form in Figure 3–2. Another kind of symmetrical arrangement can be produced in which the spheres are located in a square lattice (Figure 3–3). However, a comparison of the efficiency of

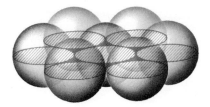

Figure 3–1   A close-packed layer of spheres.

packing for one layer shows that the hexagonal layer has a packing efficiency of 64% compared with 56% for the square-packed layer. The efficiency of packing is calculated by dividing the total volume of the spheres by the volume of the geometrical form which encloses the spheres.   The term close-packed layer is applied to the hexagonal-packed layer.

Another look at the close-packed layer (Figure 3–2) reveals that there are six triangularly shaped spaces between the close-packed spheres.   Actually, with respect to a plane through the middle of the hexagon, there are twelve such indentations, six above and six below the plane.   These will be called upper and lower cusps of a layer.   Remember this when the layers are stacked upon one another.

Now consider what happens when one close-packed layer of spheres is placed over another.   There are alternate ways to do this, but the highest efficiency of packing is obtained when the spheres of the second layer rest in the cusps of the first layer.   This is shown in an expanded diagram in Figure 3–4.   The arrows locate the occupied cusps.   Since the spheres are all of the same dimen-

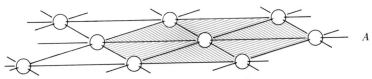

Figure 3–2   A close-packed layer of spheres expanded.

Figure 3–3   Spheres arranged in a square lattice.

sion, it is impossible to fit a sphere into each cusp.   Only three of
the six cusps can accommodate spheres of the second layer, and
these cusps will be alternate ones.   It is immaterial which group of
three cusps is selected.

Now a third layer of close-packed spheres may be placed over
the first two layers.   This may be done in two ways.   In one (Figure 3–5), the occupied upper cusps of layer B and the occupied
lower cusps of layer B are directly above one another.   Note that
the arrows point to the same triangle and that alternate cusps are
unoccupied.   Note also that the spheres of the first and third

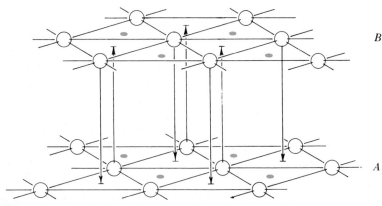

**Figure 3–4   Expanded view of the placement of the second
close-packed layer over the first close-packed layer.**

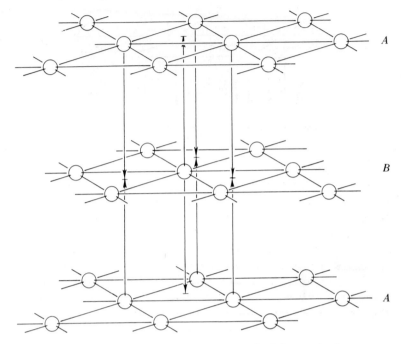

Figure 3–5 Relationship of close-packed layers in hexagonal closest packing.

layers are directly above one another. This assembly of spheres can be rotated about an axis perpendicular to the base with the result that an observer sees six identical arrangements of spheres within 360°. The structure is said to have a six-fold axis of rotation and has hexagonal symmetry. For convenience this structure is designated as $ABABAB$ . . .

In the second, the occupied upper cusps of layer B and the occupied lower cusps of layer B alternate. The unoccupied cusps must therefore also alternate (Figure 3–6). Note that the arrows now point to all the triangles of the B layer, but alternately from above and below. The symmetry of the resulting assembly of spheres is face-centered cubic, although it is difficult to see because the base of the figure is actually a plane through the corners of a

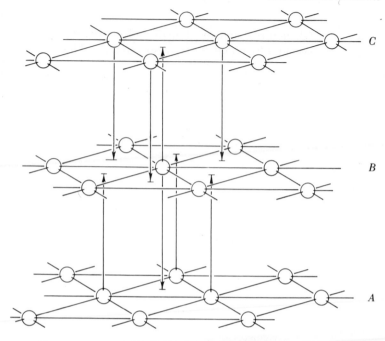

Figure 3-6   Relationship of close-packed layers in cubic closest packing.

cube (Figure 3–7). This assembly has an axis of three-fold symmetry along each body diagonal. The structure is designated as *ABCABC* . . . . These two structures represent the most efficient packing of close-packed layers of spheres (74%) and are referred to as structures with closest packing. Other combinations of these arrangements are possible but will not be discussed in this book.

Another structure results when layers in a square lattice arrangement are stacked so that the spheres of the second layer sit in the cusps of the first layer, and the spheres of the third layer reproduce the first (Figure 3–8). This is the body-centered cubic structure. It has an efficiency of packing only slightly less than that of the structures with closest packing.

In the structures with closest packing, each sphere has twelve

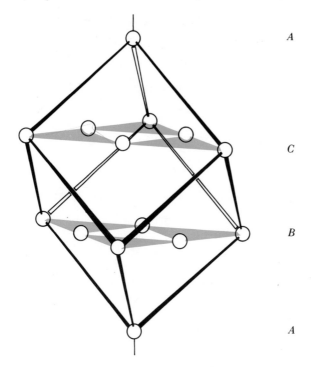

A

C

B

A

Figure 3–7   Orientation of cubic close-packed layers to show three-fold axes of symmetry which are characteristic of the cubic system.

equidistant nearest neighbors.   Each sphere is said to have a co-ordination number of twelve.   In the body-centered cubic struc-ture, each sphere has only eight equidistant neighbors.   Each sphere has a coordination number of eight.   There are six addi-tional spheres slightly further removed, and sometimes the co-ordination number is considered to be fourteen.

Tetrahedral Holes

The cusps are just as important to the interpretation of the solid state as are the spheres.   As three-dimensional structures of

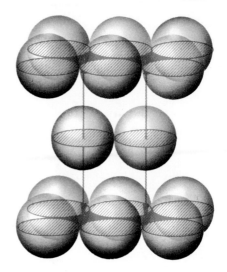

Figure 3–8   Body-centered cubic structure.

close-packed layers are built up, the enclosed cusps now constitute holes in the structure.   There are two kinds of holes created in the building process.   Each cusp which accommodates a sphere from the layer above is surrounded by four spheres in a tetrahedral arrangement (Figures 3–9, 3–10, and 3–11).   These are naturally called tetrahedral holes or voids.   Because only three of the upper cusps of layer B and similarly only three of the six lower cusps are occupied, a total of six tetrahedral holes are generated in this fashion.   However, the seventh sphere of the hexagon sits in a cusp of the upper layer as well as the lower layer, thus adding two more to make a total of eight.   By geometry it can be shown that the center of the tetrahedral holes lie at interplanar distances, $-1/4$, $+1/4$, $+3/4$, and $-3/4$ with respect to the plane through layer B.   In the hexagonal structure (Figure 3–10), the tetrahedral holes are aligned above one another to give a distorted trigonal prism with two of the holes perpendicular to the triangular faces. In the cubic structure (Figure 3–11), the tetrahedral holes between layers B and C are rotated 60° with respect to the holes below the

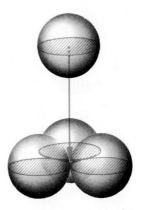

Figure 3-9   Development of a tetrahedral hole.

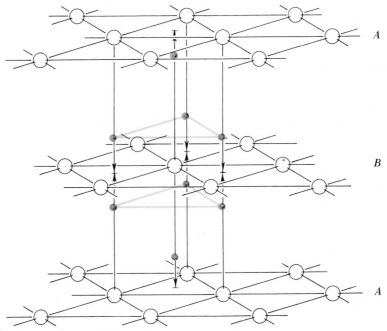

Figure 3-10   Location of tetrahedral holes in hexagonal closest packing. Colored spheres locate the holes.

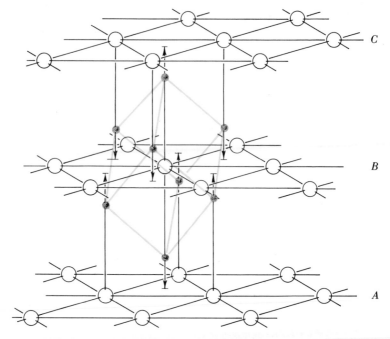

Figure 3–11 Location of tetrahedral holes in cubic closest packing. Colored spheres locate the holes. This also represents the CaF$_2$ (fluorite) type structure. All the tetrahedral holes are filled by anions. Coordination-number ratio is 8:4.

plane. The eight holes in this case sit at the corners of a cube. Now, because there are eight holes around each close-packed sphere and four spheres around each tetrahedral hole, there must be two tetrahedral holes for each close-packed sphere. This is an important fact to remember.

Octahedral Holes

There is another type of hole generated when two unoccupied cusps of adjacent layers coincide. This occurs whenever a group of three spheres arranged in an equilateral triangle overlap a similar group of three spheres with the apices of the triangles opposed [Figure 3–12(a)]. The geometrical form of these six spheres is more easily recognized if the figure is rotated as shown in Figure 3–12(b). It is now apparent why these holes are called octahedral holes.

In structures with closest packing, the coincidence of unoccupied cusps can only occur at those places where tetrahedral holes are not formed. Because there are twelve cusps per hexagonal unit, and of these, six receive spheres from adjacent layers to form tetrahedral holes, there are six left for the formation of octahedral holes. The centers of these holes are located at interplanar distances $-1/2$, and $+1/2$ with respect to a plane through layer B. Three are above and three are below the plane. In the hexagonal structure (Figure 3–13), the octahedral holes lie above one another at the corners of a trigonal prism. In the cubic case (Figure 3–14), the octahedral holes between layers B and C are rotated 60°, and now occupy corners of an octahedron. Because each hole is surrounded by six spheres and each sphere by six holes there must be one octahedral hole for each close-packed sphere. This is also an important fact to remember.

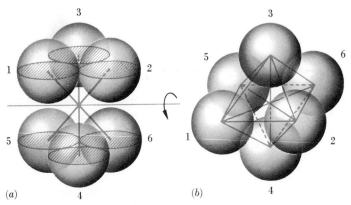

Figure 3–12 Development of an octahedral hole.

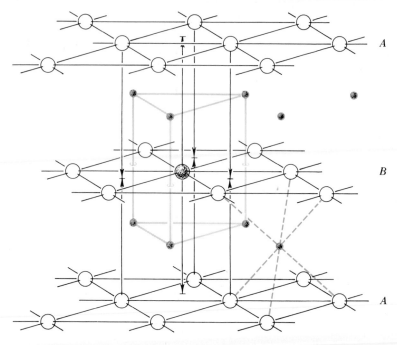

Figure 3-13 Location of octahedral holes in hexagonal closest packing. Colored spheres locate the holes. This also represents the N$_i$As type structure in which all the octahedral holes are occupied by cations. Coordination number ratio is 6:6.

Dimensional Properties of Tetrahedral and Octahedral Holes

Another important property to be considered is the size of the hole compared to the size of the close-packed spheres. The following calculations are based on the assumption that all of the close-packed spheres are in contact with one another, and that another sphere residing in the hole touches all the surrounding spheres.

The tetrahedron may be inscribed in a cube (Figure 3-15). The four spheres in an arrangement of closest packing occupy

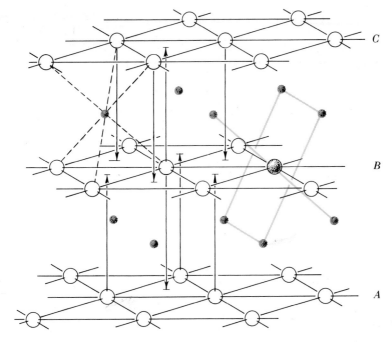

Figure 3–14 Location of octahedral holes in cubic closest packing. Colored spheres locate the holes. This also represents the NaCl type structure in which all the octahedral holes are occupied by cations. Coordination number ratio is 6:6.

four corners of the cube, and the tetrahedral hole is located at the center of the cube along the body diagonal. The face diagonal DF is twice the radius of the close-packed spheres, $2R_{cp}$, and therefore the cube edge FB may be calculated from the relationship

$$x^2 + x^2 = 4R^2_{cp}$$
$$x = \sqrt{2}R_{cp}$$

Since the body diagonal, DB, is $2R_{cp} + 2r_t$ (where r_t is the radius of the tetrahedral hole) and the angle DFB is a right angle, then

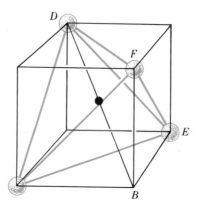

Figure 3–15 A tetrahedron inscribed in a cube.

$$(2R_{cp} + 2r_t)^2 = (2R_{cp})^2 + (\sqrt{2}R_{cp})^2$$
$$2R_{cp} + 2r_t = \sqrt{6}R_{cp}$$
$$\frac{r_t}{R_{cp}} = 0.225$$

The calculation of the maximum radius ratio for the octahedral case is more simple. Only the four spheres in the square plane need be considered (Figure 3–16). Because ABC is a right triangle, and AB and BC are equal to $(R_{cp} + r_o)$, and AC is equal to $2\,R_{cp}$, then

$$(2R_{cp})^2 = 2(R_{cp} + r_o)^2$$
$$2R_{cp} = \sqrt{2}R_{cp} + \sqrt{2}r_o$$
$$\frac{r_o}{R_{cp}} = 0.414$$

The octahedral holes thus have a radius almost twice that of the tetrahedral holes. This fact will be of considerable importance in the discussion on the structure of solid binary and ternary compounds.

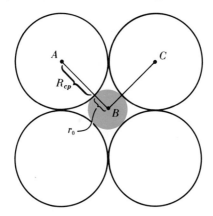

Figure 3–16   A square plane of spheres about an octahedral hole.

3–2   THE METALS

Metal atoms are essentially spherical, and therefore it is not surprising to find that the two most important structures for metals are those of hexagonal closest packing and cubic closest packing (Table 3–1). Quite a few metals also show structures in which the metal is in the body-centered cubic arrangement. It is also not surprising to find that the metals are easily transformed from one structure to another. This simply requires that the close-packed planes glide over one another to establish new positions with respect to one another. Not only should the structures be interconvertible, but metals in the cubic structure should be more easily deformed than those in the hexagonal structure, because in the cubic structure there are more planes of symmetry at which gliding may occur than in the hexagonal system. Even though the crystals are relatively easily deformed, the high melting points, boiling points, and densities of the transitional elements (Table 3–2) attest to the relatively strong metallic bonds within the crystals.

Table 3-1

Crystal Structures of the Transitional and Inner-transitional Metals*

3d elements

Sc	ccp, hcp
Ti	hcp, bcc
V	bcc
Cr	bcc, hcp
Mn	complex
Fe	ccp, bcc
Co	ccp, hcp
Ni	ccp, hcp
Cu	ccp
Zn	hcp

4d elements

Y	hcp
Zr	bcc, hcp
Nb	bcc
Mo	bcc, hcp
Tc	hcp
Ru	hcp, ccp
Rh	ccp
Pd	ccp
Ag	ccp
Cd	hcp

5d elements

La	ccp, hcp
Hf	hcp, bcc
Ta	bcc
W	bcc, complex
Re	hcp
Os	hcp, ccp
Ir	ccp
Pt	ccp
Au	ccp
Hg	complex

6d elements

Ac	ccp
Th	ccp, bcc

4f elements

Ce	Pr	Nd	Pm	Sm	Eu	Gd	Tb	Dy	Ho	Er	Tm	Yb	Lu
ccp	hex	hex	—	rhomb	bcc	hcp	hcp	hcp	hcp	hcp	hcp	ccp	hcp
bcc	bcc	bcc										bcc	

5f elements

Pa	U	Np	Pu
tetr	bcc	bcc	bcc	mono
	ortho	ortho	ccp
	tetr	tetr	ortho
			tetra

*Abbreviations:

ccp	cubic close packed	hex	hexagonal
hcp	hexagonal close packed	rhomb	rombohedral
bcc	body centered cubic	mono	monoclinic
tetr	tetragonal		
ortho	orthorhombic		

76

Table 3–2

The Physical Properties of the Transitional Elements and Inner-transitional Elements (Temperature °C)

	mp	bp	d		mp	bp	d		mp	bp	d		mp	bp	d
Sc	1539	2727	2.99	Y	1500	2927	4.48	La	920	3469	6.18	Ac	1050	—	—
Ti	1677	3277	4.49	Zr	1855	4474	6.25	Hf	2222	5280	13.31	Th	1750	—	11.7
V	1710	3000	5.96	Nb	2487	4930	8.58	Ta	2997	5400	16.69				
Cr	1550	2642	7.2	Mo	2610	4830	10.2	W	3377	5527	19.1				
Mn	1244	2041	7.21	Tc	2127	—	11.50	Re	3180	5630	20.9				
Fe	1530	2887	7.86	Ru	1950	3727	12.30	Os	2727	4230	22.7				
Co	1490	2877	8.83	Rh	1966	3729	12.42	Ir	2454	4130	22.65				
Ni	1452	2810	8.90	Pd	1550	3127	12.03	Pt	1769	3827	21.45				
Cu	1084	2582	8.92	Ag	960.5	2177	10.50	Au	1063	2707	19.3				
Zn	419.4	906	7.13	Cd	320.9	765	8.64	Hg	−38.87	356.6	13.59				

	Ce	Pr	Nd	Pm	Sm	Eu	Gd	Tb	Dy	Ho	Er	Tm	Yb	Lu
mp	775	935	1024	—	1072	826	1312	1356	1407	1461	1497	1545	824	1652
bp	3468	3127	3027	—	1900	1439	3000	2800	2600	2600	2900	1727	1427	2173
d	8.23	6.78	7.00	—	7.54	5.26	7.90	8.27	8.54	8.80	9.05	9.33	6.98	9.84

	Pa	U	Np	Pu	Am
mp	<1873	1132	640	637.5	850
bp	—	3818	—	3235	2607
d	15.37	19.04	20.45	19.74	11.87

3–3 ALLOYS

Substitutional Alloys

The simplest alloy is that in which atoms of one metal are replaced with atoms of another element. These are called substitutional alloys. This replacement process extends over the whole range of compositions if certain conditions are met: the atomic radii must not differ by more than 15%, the elements must crystallize in the same crystal system, and the metal must exhibit the same relative valency and chemical properties. Alloys of this type are expected for the elements within the same group, especially between the $4d$ and $5d$ elements. Examples are Cu–Ni, Au–Ag, and Mo–W. If any of these conditions are violated only a limited amount of one element will dissolve in the other before a new phase separates out.

Intermediate Phase or Hume-Rothery Compounds

Hume-Rothery, an English scientist, pointed out in 1926 that many binary metal systems have intermediate phases which can be classified according to their atom:valence electron ratio. Alloys of three characteristic ratios are known, namely, $14:21$, $13:21$, and $12:21$. Some examples are listed in Table 3–3. Note that there is no obvious relationship in the stoichiometry between the alloys of a given class. The number of valence electrons is taken from the

Table 3–3

Alloys which Conform to the Hume-Rothery Atom/Valence Electron Ratios

14/21	13/21	12/21
CuZn	Cu_5Zn	$CuZn_3$
Cu_3Al	Cu_9Al_4	Cu_5Al_3
Cu_5Sn	$Cu_{31}Sn_8$	Cu_3Sn
AgCd	Ni_5Zn_{21}	$FeZn_7$

ground-state description (Table 1–2), being 1 for copper (s^1), 2 for zinc (s^2), 3 for aluminum (s^2p^1), and 4 for tin (s^2p^2). Elements of the iron and platinum groups form such alloys, but to place them in this classification, the metal valence must be taken as zero (s^0). The ratios are calculated as follows. The alloy Cu_5Sn has six atoms and $(5 \times 1) + (1 \times 4) = 9$ valence electrons. The ratio of atoms to number of valence electrons reduces to $2/3$ which is equivalent to $14/21$ when expressed in the common demoninator 21. This will not be developed further here.

Interstitial Alloys

The hydrides, borides, nitrides, and carbides of the transitional elements have metallic properties and are frequently referred to as alloys. These nonmetals have small covalent radii and, as expected, occupy either the tetrahedral or octahedral holes in the metal.

The nitrides and carbides, especially of groups four and five, form interstitial compounds in which all the octahedral holes of a cubic close-packed metal structure are filled, giving a NaCl type structure. The carbides adopt the cubic close-packed structure whether or not the metals were of this original structure. Substitutional solid solutions of these compounds may also be formed by replacing the metal atoms with atoms of a second metal. Tungsten and molybdenum form nitrides of composition M_2N in which only one-half of the octahedral holes are occupied, while in Mn_4N and Fe_4N one-fourth of the octahedral holes are occupied. The complex iron-carbon system has been studied in detail, but only two of the carbides, austentite and cementite, will be mentioned here. The interstitial solid solution of carbon in gamma Fe (stable from 910° to 1400°) is called austentite. Here the carbon atoms occupy octahedral voids of the cubic close-packed iron atoms. The intermediate phase Fe_3C, called cementite, has each carbon atom in the center of a distorted trigonal prism of six iron atoms. Each iron atom must be common to two carbons in order to maintain the 3:1 ratio.

The hydrides of the transitional elements form compounds in which the hydrogens occupy all the tetrahedral holes in TiH_2 and

CrH_2 (fluorite structure), one-half the tetrahedral holes in ZrH and TiH (zinc blende structure), and one-fourth and one-eighth of the tetrahedral holes in Pd_2H and Zr_4H, respectively. The hydrogen can be reversibly absorbed and desorbed, thus resulting in products of non-whole-number stoichiometry. The hydrides of the $4f$ and $5f$ elements have compositions such as $LaH_{2.76}$, $PrH_{2.85}$, and UH_3. Their heats of formation are comparable to those of the s element hydrides, although like the d element hydrides, they are less dense than the parent metal. Thus the f metal hydrides seem to represent an intermediate type of compound.

The borides of the transitional elements are high melting and conductors of electricity. They form a wider variety of compounds than do the nitrides, carbides, and hydrides, presumably due to the formation of boron-boron bonds. The borides such as FeB, CoB, and ZrB consist of metal atoms at the corners of a trigonal prism with a boron atom at the center. Because the atomic ratio is $1:1$, each metal atom must also be common to six borons. The boron-boron distance is shorter than the metal-boron distance, suggesting that the borons are bonded. The borides of composition TiB_2, VB_2, and TaB_2 have the metals in a hexagonal close-packed layer sandwiched in between layers of hexagonally arranged boron atoms. Again, each boron sits at the center of a trigonal prism of metal atoms with each metal bonded to three borons to preserve the $1:2$ ratio. Another interesting class of borides are those of formula MB_6. The $4f$ elements in particular form these unusual compounds, as in LaB_6, CeB_6, and YbB_6. In these compounds, the octahedral B_6 unit sits in the center of a simple cube of metal atoms; thus, the coordination number of the B_6 unit is eight. To maintain the ratio of $1:1$, each metal must also be common to eight B_6 units which are also at the corners of a simple cube. The entire structure may be considered as made up of two inter-penetrating simple cubic structures of B_6^{3-} and M^{3+} ions.

3–4   STRUCTURES OF BINARY COMPOUNDS

The structures of binary compounds may be considered as consisting of halide or oxide ions in closest packing with the cations occupying either the tetrahedral or octahedral holes. Ideally the size of the cation:anion ratio determines which kind of hole is occupied, the small cations in the tetrahedral, and the large cations in the octahedral holes. The number of holes occupied is determined by the stoichiometry of the compound and the ratio of holes to close-packed atoms.

The compound MX has an atomic ratio of 1:1, and this requires that all the octahedral holes be occupied by cations because there are as many octahedral holes as close-packed ions. Sodium chloride is the prototype of this class in the cubic symmetry (Figure 3–14), and nickel arsenide (Figure 3–13) is an example of this class in the hexagonal system. Examples of the transitional element compounds which crystallize in these systems are listed in Table 3–4. Now, if the cation is small enough to occupy tetrahedral holes, then to maintain the stoichiometry of 1:1, only one-half of the tetrahedral holes are occupied because there are twice the number of tetrahedral holes as there are close-packed atoms. This allows some choice of occupancy. In zinc sulfide, the zinc ions take positions in which they themselves form a tetrahedron. Zinc sulfide exists both in the cubic system (Figure 3–17) and the hexagonal system (Figure 3–18). Note that the only difference in the cation occupancy is in the way the tetrahedrons are oriented with respect to one another. Table 3–4 includes examples of transitional element compounds which crystallize with these structures.

The composition MX_2 is represented by several different structures. The cadmium chloride structure (Figure 3–19) has anions in cubic-closest packing, while cadmium iodide (Figure 3–20) has the anions in hexagonal-closest packing. Note that in general the larger anions prefer the hexagonal structure (Table 3–4). In both cases, only one-half of the octahedral holes are occupied. There is a choice of hole occupancy for structures in which the holes are only partially filled, and it appears that the directional (covalent character) nature of the bond dictates the preferential filling. In these structures, the hole occupancy is such that all the holes in one layer are filled, and all the holes in the next layer are empty. Such a structure is commonly called a layer lattice, and the physical properties of the solid reflect the weak forces between the anion layers. It is important to remember that the ratio of the

Table 3–4

Structures of Binary Transitional Element Halides and Oxides

Type Compound	Cation : Anion Coordination Number Ratio	Fraction and Type of Holes Occupied	Examples Closest Packing Cubic	Examples Closest Packing Hexagonal
MX	6:6	All octahedral holes	*NaCl* TiO, VO, MnO, FeO, CoO, CrN, MnS, EuS, AgF, AgCl, AgBr, TiC	*NiAs* PtSe, MnSe, CrS, CoS, FeS, NiS
	4:4	One-half tetrahedral holes	ZnS (Zinc blende) AgSb, CuBr, CuI, CuCl, AgI	ZnS (wurtzite)
MX$_2$	6:3	One-half octahedral holes Layer lattice	*CdCl$_2$* FeCl$_2$, CoCl$_2$, NiCl$_2$, MnCl$_2$, NiI$_2$	*CdI$_2$* MnI$_2$, FeI$_2$, CoI$_2$, FeBr$_2$, CoBr$_2$, NiBr$_2$
	6:3	Distorted body centered-cubic One-half of the octahedral holes occupied throughout the three dimensions cation : anion < 0.7	*TiO$_2$* MnO$_2$, MnF$_2$, FeF$_2$, CoF$_2$, NiF$_2$, VO$_2$, NbO$_2$, WO$_2$, MoO$_2$, PdF$_2$, RuO$_2$, OsO$_2$	—
	8:4	All tetrahedral holes cation : anion > 0.7 Cations in closest packing.	*CaF$_2$* ZrO$_2$, ThO$_2$, CeO$_2$, PrO$_2$, EuF$_2$, UO$_2$, AmO$_2$, LaOF, CuF$_2$, HfO$_2$, AcOF	—

82

Table 3-4 (continued)

Type Compound	Cation : Anion Coordination Number Ratio	Fraction and Type of Holes Occupied	Examples Closest Packing	
			Cubic	Hexagonal
MX_3	6:2	One-third octahedral holes Two-thirds of sites in alternate layers. Layer lattice	$CrCl_3$ $RuCl_3$	BiI_3 $FeBr_3, FeCl_3$ $CrBr_3, ScCl_3$
	6:2	One-third of octahedral holes occupied in every layer to give metal ion chains	—	$\beta\text{-}TiCl_3$ $TiBr_3, ZrBr_3, ZrI_3,$ $HfBr_3, HfI_3$
	6:3	One-third of octahedral holes occupied through three dimensions	ScF_3 $AcF_3, CeF_3, FeF_3, UF_3,$ CoF_3, RhF_3, PrF_3	—
MX_4	6:6/4	One-fourth of octahedral holes occupied to form metal chains	—	NbI_4
	4:1	One-eighth of tetrahedral holes occupied	SnI_4 $ThCl_4, UCl_4, ZrBr_4,$ $TiBr_4, TiI_4, ZrI_4,$ $HfI_4, HfBr_4, Zr_4H$	—
MX_5	6:6/5	One-fifth of octahedral holes filled to form M_2X_{10} molecular units	—	$MoCl_5, NbCl_5$ $TaCl_5$
MX_6	6:1	One-sixth of octahedral holes filled to form MX_6 molecules	—	UCl_6, WCl_6

Table 3-4 (continued)

Type Compound	Cation : Anion Coordination Number Ratio	Fraction and Type of Holes Occupied	Examples Closest Packing	
			Cubic	Hexagonal
M_2O_3	6:4	Two-thirds of octahedral holes through three dimensions	—	αAl_2O_3 Fe_2O_3, Cr_2O_3 Ti_2O_3, V_2O_3, Rh_2O_3
	6:4	Cations in closest packing Three-fourths of tetrahedral holes occupied by oxides	C type Mn_2O_3, Sc_2O_3 Re_2O_3	—
MO_3	6:2	One-fourth of octahedral holes occupied by metals. Only three-fourths of oxide ion sites occupied	ReO_3, WO_3	—

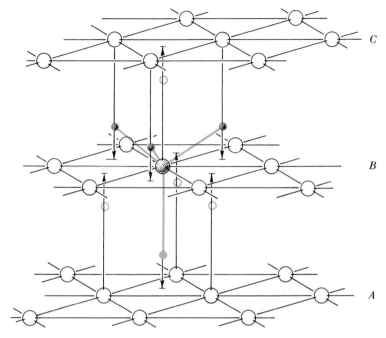

Figure 3–17   ZnS, zinc blende type structure.   Cubic closest packing of anions.   One-half of all the tetrahedral holes occupied.   Coordination number ratio of 4:4.   Filled holes are colored; empty holes are white.

coordination numbers must yield the same number as the ratio of atoms in the compound.   Here the coordination number of the anion must be three.   The three metal ions are common to one halogen and form the base of a trigonal pyramid which has a halogen at the apex.

Another structure with coordination number ratio of 6:3 for compounds of MX_2 composition is the rutile (TiO_2) structure. This is not a system with closest packing, but is a distorted body-centered cubic structure (tetragonal).   The titanium ions are surrounded octahedrally by oxide ions, and each oxide ion is bonded to three titantium ions which are coplanar and at the corners of an

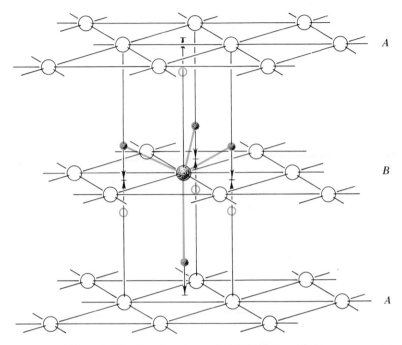

Figure 3-18 ZnS, wurtzite type structure. Hexagonal closest packing of anions. One-half of all the tetrahedral holes occupied. Coordination number ratio of 4:4. Filled holes are colored; empty holes are white.

equilateral triangle (Figure 3-21). One-half of the octahedral holes must be empty, but they are distributed throughout the three dimensions rather than being confined to a given layer. This structure is typical for the oxides and fluorides of the smaller M(IV) cations. The role of the radius ratio is observed here, the rutile structure being assumed when the cation:anion ratio is less than 0.7. For larger radius ratios, the fluorite structure (CaF$_2$) is favored (Figure 3-11). Here the cations are in a cubic close-packed array, and the anions occupy all the tethrahedral holes. Thus, the cations have the coordination number of eight and the anions the coordination number of four.

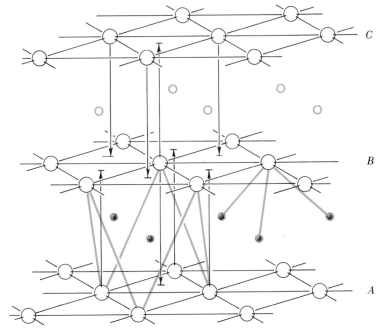

Figure 3–19 CdCl₂ type structure. Cubic closest packing of anions. One-half of the octahedral holes filled with alternate layers empty. Coordination number ratio 6:3. Filled holes are colored, empty holes are white.

Still another MX_2 structure is that of palladium (II) chloride. Here the 4-coordinated metal atoms are bridged by chloro groups to give infinite flat chains.

Compounds of composition MX_3 also present a choice of packing and hole occupancy. The chromium trichloride structure has the anions in cubic closest packing, and the bismuth triiodide structure has the anions in hexagonal closest packing. In both cases, one-third of the octahedral holes are occupied but distributed in such a way that two-thirds of the sites in alternate layers are occupied, thus again generating a layer lattice. Each cation has a coordination number of six, and therefore each anion must have a

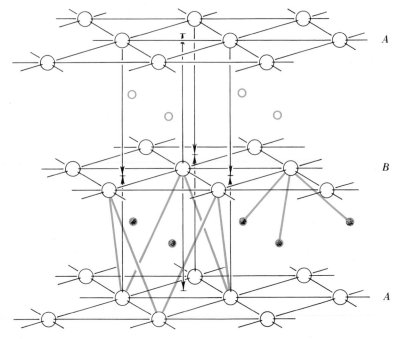

Figure 3–20   CdI₂ type structure. Hexagonal closest packing of anions.   One-half of the octahedral holes occupied.
Alternate layers are empty.   Coordination number ratio
6:3.   Filled holes are colored; empty holes are white.

coordination number of two.   An alternate type of octahedral hole
occupancy is found in titanium trichloride.   Again, only one-third
of the octahedral holes are occupied, but they are distributed
throughout the layers of hexagonal close-packed anions so that
linear chains of titanium ions result, rather than layers.   Still another distribution is found in the compound ScF₃.   Here the fluorides are approximately close-packed, and the metal ions occupy
one-third of the octahedral sites throughout the three dimensions,
but still so that each fluoride ion is common to two metal ions.

The composition MX₄ compounds are presently known in at
least two arrangements.   If the cation is relatively large, it sits in

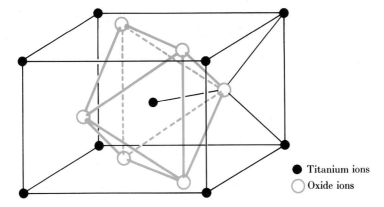

● Titanium ions
○ Oxide ions

Figure 3–21   TiO$_2$, rutile type structure.   A distorted body center cubic structure with one-half of the octahedral holes occupied throughout three dimensions.   Coordination number ratio 6:3.

an octahedral hole. This requires that one-fourth of the octahedral holes be occupied and that on the average each halogen have a coordination number of 6:4. Such a coordination number can only mean the sharing of edges of the halogen octahedra. In NbI$_4$, infinite chains of NbI$_6$ octahedra share two opposite edges. The niobium atoms occupy one-fourth of the octahedral holes to form linear chains by filling every other row of octahedral holes in every other layer. This results in adjacent occupied holes. For compounds in which the radius ratio is less than about 0.4, the tetrahedral holes rather than the octahedral holes should be occupied. This occurs in the SnCl$_4$ structure in which the chlorides are close-packed and the cations occupy one-eighth of the tetrahedral holes to give discrete molecular units. Some of the transitional metal halides which have this structure are listed in Table 3–4.

Compounds of composition MX$_5$ and MX$_6$ can also be derived from close-packed anion structures in which one-fifth and one-sixth of the octahedral holes are occupied. Because the metal in each case has a coordination number of six, the halogen in the MX$_5$ case must have an average coordination number of 6/5. This means that two MX_6 octahedra must share a common edge, thus resulting in M_2X_{10} molecular units. Examples of this are $MoCl_5$ and $NbCl_5$. In the MX_6 case, molecular units are formed since the coordination numbers, and numbers of atoms in the molecule are identical. WCl_6 and UCl_6 are examples of this kind of structure.

Several classes of oxides still need consideration. The composition M_2O_3 is represented by several alternate structures. In corundum, $\alpha = Al_2O_3$, the oxide ions are in hexagonal closest-packing with the cations occupying two-thirds of the octahedral holes, distributed throughout three dimensions. Since the cations have the coordination number six, the anions must have the coordination number four. Manganese (III) oxide (Figure 3–22) is typical of

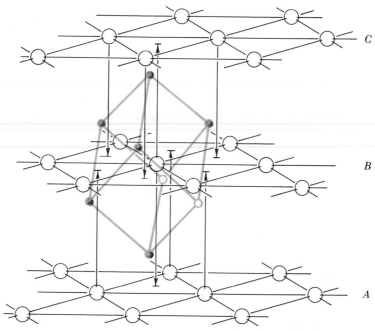

Figure 3–22 Mn_2O_3 structure. Cubic closest-packing of Mn(III) ions. Three-fourths of tetrahedral sites occupied by oxide ions. Face diagonal vacancies shown. Cation coordination number is six, anion coordination number is four.

another M_2O_3 structure (Table 3–4). Here the cation is in cubic closest packing (note the similarity to the CaF_2 structure, Figure 3–11), and the oxide ions occupy three-fourths of the tetrahedral sites. There are eight tetrahedral holes per close-packed cation, and six of these are occupied by oxide ions. The two vacancies occur at the ends of a face diagonal for one-half of the M(III) ions, and at the ends of a body diagonal for the other half of the M(III) ions. The third structure of some importance is typified by ReO_3. Instead of a complete cubic close-packed layer of oxide ions, one-fourth of the positions are vacant. The metal atoms occupy only one-fourth of the octahedral sites in order to achieve the atom ratio of 1:3. Since the metal coordination is six, the oxygen coordination number must be two. These two metal sites are arranged linearly. This structure is the same as the perovskite structure except that the cation which occupies the site of twelve coordination is absent. (See Section 3–5, Figure 3–23)

3–5   THE STRUCTURES OF TERNARY COMPOUNDS

Perovskites—ABC_3

The mineral perovskite $CaTiO_3$ is the prototype of a general class of compounds identified by that name. The structure consists of oxide and calcium ions in cubic closest packing, with calcium ions making up one-fourth of the close-packed sites (Figure 3–23). There is one titanium ion per four close-packed ions, and therefore the titanium ions must be present in one-fourth of the octahedral holes. There are no titanate ions as such, although that nomenclature is commonly used. Each calcium ion has twelve nearest oxide ions, and each oxygen has four nearest calciums. Other compounds of the transitional elements with this or some slight distortion in the structure are listed in Table 3–5. Note that the sum of the oxidation states of the cation is always six.

Special note should be made of the interesting compound $NaWO_3$ and its reduction products which are commonly called tungsten bronzes. This compound has the perovskite structure in which the sodium ion occupies the site of twelve coordination. Products can be prepared which are deficient in sodium but have

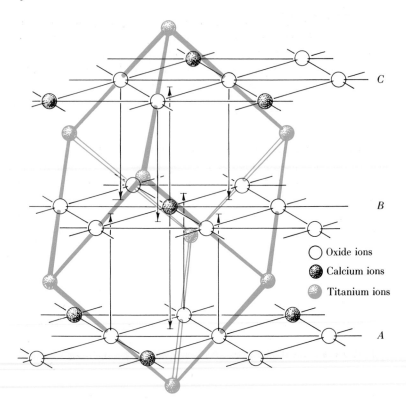

Figure 3–23 The perovoskite structure. Cubic closest packing of oxide layers. Titanium ions occupy one-fourth of the octahedral holes.

Legend within figure:
○ Oxide ions
◉ Calcium ions
◉ Titanium ions

Table 3–5

Example of Compounds with Perovskite Structures

Type	$(1^+, 5^+)$	$(2^+, 4^+)$	$(3^+, 3^+)$
Formula	$NaNbO_3$	$SrTiO_3$	$LaTiO_3$
	$AgTaO_3$	$CaZrO_3$	$LaCrO_3$
	$NaWO_3$	$BaThO_3$	$LaMnO_3$
		$BaCeO_3$	$LaFeO_3$

the same structure. This means that some of the sodium sites are vacant and that the average oxidation state of the tungsten must be between five and six to maintain electrical neutrality. These products have intense colors ranging from yellow to red, violet, and purple as the sodium content decreases.

The Ilmenite Structure—ABC_3

Ilmenite has the same general formula $FeTiO_3$ as a perovskite, but it consists of oxide ions in hexagonal closest packing, with titanium (IV) and iron (II) ions occupying two-thirds of the octahedral holes. As with the perovskite structure, there are no discrete TiO_3^{2-} ions as such, and the sum of the cation valencies total six. This structure is favored for ions smaller than those found in the perovskite structure. Compounds of this type are $MnTiO_3$, $CoTiO_3$, and $NiTiO_3$.

Spinels—AB_2O_4

The mineral spinel has the formula $MgAl_2O_4$. Its structure consists of cubic closest-packed oxide ions, with the metal ions distributed between one-eighth of the tetrahedral holes and one-half of the octahedral holes. Here again there are no discrete $Al_2O_4^{2-}$

Table 3–6
Examples of Compounds with Spinel Structures

	Formula	Tetrahedral Hole	Octahedral Hole
Normal	$FeAl_2O_4$	Fe (II)	Al (III)
	$MgCr_2O_4$	Mg (II)	Cr (III)
	$ZnFe_2O_4$	Zn (II)	Fe (III)
Inverse	$CuFe_2O_4$	Fe (III)	Cu (II) Fe (III)
	$TiZn_2O_4$	Zn (II)	Zn (II) Ti (IV)
	$SnCo_2O_4$	Co (II)	Co (II) Sn (IV)

units in the crystal. In these compounds, the positive charge must total eight, but this can be satisfied by combinations of two trivalent ions and one divalent ion, or two divalent ions and a tetravalent ion. Normal spinels have the trivalent B-ion in octahedral holes and the divalent A-ion in tetrahedral holes. The so-called inverse spinels have the B-ion in both the holes and the A-ion in the octahedral holes. Examples of spinels are given in Table 3–6.

3–6 THE RELATIONSHIP OF STRUCTURE TO PHYSICAL PROPERTIES

Melting points and boiling points are related to the forces which must be overcome in converting the species of the solid phase into the species of the liquid phase and the forces involved in converting the species of the liquid phase into the gaseous phase. These forces, in turn, are related to the energy required to break chemical bonds and the number of bonds to be broken in changing states. Much is known about the structures of solids, but unfortunately not much is known about the nature of species in the molten state. More is known about the nature of species evaporated into the gaseous state, and the surprising thing here is the complexity of the species found in the vapor phase. However, to simplify the argument here, the assumption will be made that the species evaporated corresponds to the simplest formula.

The cations of compounds in which the anion exists in closest packing are present either in six-coordination in octahedral holes or, if the cations are small enough, in four-coordination in tetrahedral holes. If we consider an element M which can exist in a multiplicity of oxidation states to form the compounds MX to MX_6, the trend in increasing volatility with oxidation state can be rationalized as follows: In each instance the environment about the metal is identical; assume that even $M(VI)$ is large enough to occupy an octahedral hole. To preserve the stoichiometry in MX, all the octahedral holes are filled, in MX_2 one-half the octahedral holes, in MX_3 one-third the octahedral holes, in MX_4 one-fourth the octahedral holes, in MX_5 one-fifth, and in MX_6 one-sixth of the octahedral holes. There is more than one way in which the cation can occupy the holes except for the MX compound in which all the holes are occupied. Whatever this way may be, the anion coordination number on the average must be three for MX_2, two for MX_3, 6/4 for MX_4, 6/5 for MX_5, and 1 for MX_6. The fractional numbers have been accounted for in Section 3–4.

Now what happens as molecular units are separated out of the crystal lattice? In the highest oxidation state, the coordination number of the cation and anion are identical with the number of atoms in the simplest formula. A molecule exists as such in the solid with only the forces between the molecular units holding the crystal together. These forces are weak, and the compound would be expected to be very volatile, and it is (Table 3–7). In all other cases, however, metal-halogen bonds must be broken in order to separate out MX, MX_2, MX_3, MX_4, and MX_5 units. One would expect that the energy required to break a M(V)—X bond would be greater than for a M(I)—X bond. On this basis MX_5 might be expected to be less volatile than MX_4, but generally this is not the case. What is more important is the number of metal-halogen bonds which must be broken. Thus, to separate a MX unit from a MX_6 octahedron in the crystal, five M—X bonds must be ruptured, and because the X of the MX unit is also associated with five M atoms in addition to the one of the MX unit, an additional five X—M bonds must be broken for a total of ten. To separate a MX_2 unit from the MX_6 octahedron in the crystal, four M—X bonds must be broken; but, in addition, because each X is bonded to two other M atoms in addition to the one in the MX_2 unit, four additional X—M bonds are broken for a total of eight. In separating a MX_3 unit from the MX_6 octahedron in the crystal, three M—X bonds are broken, but since each X is associated with one other M in addition to the one of the MX_3 unit, three more X—M bonds are broken for a total of six. Similarly for the MX_4 unit, only two M—X bonds are broken, but each X is associated on the average with one-half of a metal atom in addition to the one in the MX_4 unit. This requires that two additional X—M bonds be broken for a total of four. Finally, in the separation of a MX_5 unit from the MX_6 octahedron of the crystal, only one M—X bond is broken, but each X atom is bonded on the average to an additional one-fifth of a metal atom, and thus the total M—X

Table 3–7
Melting Points and Boiling Points of Transitional Element Halides and Oxides (°C)

	mp	bp		mp	bp		mp	bp
3d ScF_3	(1227)	(1527)	3d MnF_2	856	(2027)	4d ZrF_2	(1402) disp	
$ScCl_3$	960	967	$MnCl_2$	650	1290	$ZrCl_2$	(727) disp	
$ScBr_3$	960	929	$MnBr_2$	698	(1027)	$ZrBr_2$	(627) disp	
ScI_3	945	909	MnI_2	638	(827)	ZrI_2	(427) disp	
TiF_4	290 s	(327)	FeF_3	1027	(1327)	NbF_5	75	234.9
$TiCl_4$	−24.1	236	$FeCl_3$	306	d	$NbCl_5$	212	243
$TiBr_4$	38.3	230	$FeBr_3$	(227)	(627)	$NbBr_5$	227	272
TiI_4	155	377	FeF_2	1102	1827	NbI_5	(327) d	
TiF_3	(1227)	(1727)	$FeCl_2$	677	1026	MoF_6	17	36
$TiCl_3$	700 disp		$FeBr_2$	684	(927)	MoF_5	77	213.6
$TiBr_3$	(927) disp		FeI_2	587	(827)	$MoCl_5$	194	268
TiI_3	(927) disp		CoF_3	(1027)	(1327)	$MoCl_4$	(317)	(322)
TiF_2	(1277)	(2152)	CoF_2	1202	(1727)	$MoBr_4$	(337)	(347)
$TiCl_2$	(677)	(1479)	$CoCl_2$	727	1050	MoI_4	(417)	(422)
$TiBr_2$	(627)	(1227)	$CoBr_2$	678	(927)	TcF_6	33.4	55.3
TiI_2	(627)	(1027)	CoI_2	517	(827)	RuF_6	54	200
VF_5	(102)	(111)	NiF_2	(1027)	(1627)	RuF_5	101	272
VF_4	(327) d		$NiCl_2$	1001	987	$RuCl_3$	627 d	
VCl_4	−26	164 d	$NiBr_2$	963		$RuBr_3$	600 d	
VBr_4	27	247	NiI_2	797	(747)	RuI_3	127 d	
VF_3	(1127)	(1427)	CuF_2	(927)	(1527)	RhF_4	550 s	
VCl_3		disp	$CuCl_2$	537 d		RhF_3	1127	1227
VBr_3		d	$CuBr_2$	327 d		$RhCl_3$	948 d	
VF_2	(1127)	(2227)	CuF		disp	$RhBr_3$	527 d	
VCl_2	1000	(1377)	$CuCl$	430	1690	RhI_3	327 d	
VBr_2	(827)	(1227)	$CuBr$	488	852	PdF_3	227 d	
VI_2	(777)	(927)	CuI	588	1293	PdF_2	727	1227
CrF_6	−80 d		4d YF_3	(1387)	(2227)	$PdCl_2$	678	
CrF_5	100 s		YCl_3	700	(1507)	$PdBr_2$	(627)	
CrF_4	200 s		YBr_3	904	(1467)	PdI_2	(427)	
CrF_3	1100	(1427)	YI_3	1000	1307	AgF_2	690	
$CrCl_3$	1152	1047	ZrF_4	912		AgF	435	
$CrBr_3$	(1127)		$ZrCl_4$	437 p	331 s	$AgCl$	445	1554
CrI_3	500 d		$ZrBr_4$	450 p	357 s	$AgBr$	430	(1537)
CrF_2	1102	(2127)	ZrI_4	499 p	431 s	AgI	557	1506
$CrCl_2$	815	1302	ZrF_3	(1327) disp		5d LaF_3	(1427)	(2327)
$CrBr_2$	842	(1127)	$ZrCl_3$	(627) disp		$LaCl_3$	852	(1747)
CrI_2	793	(827)	$ZrBr_3$	(827) disp		$LaBr_3$	783	(1577)
MnF_3	(1077)		ZrI_3	(927) disp		LaI_3	761	(1402)

Table 3-7 (*Continued*)

	mp	bp		mp	bp		mp	bp
l HfF₄	(927)		5d AuF₃	727 d		3d TiO₂	1855	2927 d
HfCl₄	522 p	317 s	AuCl₃	288	427 d	Ti₂O₃	2127	3027
HfBr₄	420 p	322 s	AuCl	287 d		V₂O₅	670	(1827)
HfI₄	(477) p	(427)s	AuBr	212 d		VO₂	1545	2727 d
TaF₅	97	229.2	AuI	177 d		V₂O₃	1967	3027 d
TaCl₅	207	334	6d AcF₃	(1327)	(2277)	CrO₃	1187	
TaBr₅	280.2	348.8	AcCl₃	(927)	(1757)	CrO₂	427 d	
TaI₅	543	496	AcBr₃	(827)	(1597)	Cr₂O₃	2437	3027
WF₆	2.0	17.1	AcI₃	(827)	(1407)	MnO₂	847	
WCl₆	284.0	336.5	ThF₄	(1327)	(2277)	Mn₂O₃	1347 d	
WBr₆	309	d	ThCl₄	(765)	(922)	MnO	185	3127 d
WF₅	(107)	268	ThBr₄	679	857	Fe₂O₃	1457 d	
WCl₅	230	286	ThI₄	566	837	Fe₃O₄	1597	1787 d
WBr₅	295	392	4f CeF₃	1430	(2327)	FeO	1377 d	
WF₄	800 d		CeCl₃	820	(1730)	Co₃O₄	1967 d	
WCl₄	477 d		CeBr₃	732	(1560)	CoO	1805 d	
ReF₇	48.3		CeI₃	752	740	4d NiO	1957	
ReF₆	18.8	35.6	GdF₃	1231	(2277)	CuO	1336	
ReCl₆	22	d	GdCl₃	690	(1580)	Cu₂O	1229	
ReF₅	48	221.3	GdBr₃	765	(1490)	Y₂O₃	2417	4297
ReCl₅	(275)	(327)	GdI₃	926	(1340)	ZrO₂	2677	4297
ReF₄	124.5	795	YbF₃	(1157)	(2227)	Nb₂O₅	1512	
ReCl₃	(727)	(827)	YbCl₃	854	d	MoO₃	795	1257
ReBr₃	627	(727)	YbBr₃	940	d	MoO₂	1977 d	
OsF₆	32.1	47.0	TBI₃	(1027)	d	Tc₂O₇	119.6	583
OsF₅	70	225.9	5f UF₆		−56.54	RuO₄	27 d	
OsF₄	(230) d		UCl₆	179 d		RuO₂	955	1127 d
OsCl₄	(323) d		UF₅		d	Rh₂O₃	1115 d	
IrF₆	44.4	53.0	UCl₅	327 d		PdO	1877 d	
IrF₄	106	300	UF₄	960		Ag₂O	200 d	
IrCl₃	765 d		UCl₄	590	792	5d La₂O₃	2317	4197
IrBr₃	d		UBr₄	519	761	HfO₂	2790	
IrI₃	427 d		UI₄	506	756	Ta₂O₅	1877	
PtF₆	56.7		UCl₃	842		WO₃	1472	1667
PtF₅	76	300	UBr₃	730		WO₂	1852 d	
PtF₄	627		UI₃	680		Re₂O₇	300 d	360.3
PtCl₃	435 d		NpF₆		55.18	ReO₃	160	
PtBr₃	405 d		PuF₆		62.16	OsO₄	42	130
PtI₃	270 d		PuF₄	1037		OsO₂	650 d	
PtCl₂	581 d		PuF₃	1425		IrO₂	1100	
PtBr₂	410 d		PuCl₃	760		PtO	507 d	
PtI₂	327 d		PuBr₃	681		Au₂O₃		d

d = decomposes, *disp* = disproportionation, *s* = sublimes, *p* = under pressure, ( ) means estimated value.

bonds broken will be two. These data are summarized in Table
3–8. Therefore, simply on the basis of the total number of bonds
to be broken, one would expect MX_6 to be the most volatile compound of the group and MX to be the least volatile. The nature of
the bond need not be invoked except to the extent that it is important in determining which holes are occupied when alternate arrangements are possible. Compounds with layer lattices would be
expected to be more volatile than compounds with the same atom
ratio but with the octahedral holes occupied throughout the three
dimensions. The layers are simply held by weak anion interactions and therefore are more easily separated than their three-
dimensional counterparts. One must conclude, however, that the
layer lattice compounds probably evaporate as polymers, because
to evaporate molecules of the simplest formula, the same total
number of bonds must be broken for a given atom ratio regardless
of the cation distribution in the lattice.

Compounds of the composition MX_4 may be discussed in the
same manner. When a cation of oxidation state four occupies a
tetrahedral hole, the anion has a coordination number of one and a
neutral molecule exists in the solid. Again, only weak intermolecu-
lar forces are involved in holding the molecules together in the

Table 3–8
Bonds Broken in the Separation of a MX_n Unit from a MX_6 Structure

Composition	Coordination Number Cation	Anion	Number of Bonds Broken to Separate Molecular Species
MX_6	6	1	0
MX_5	6	6/5	2
MX_4	6	6/4	4
MX_3	6	2	6
MX_2	6	3	8
MX	6	6	10

crystal, and the substance is easily volatilized. Nothing need be said about the per cent covalent character of these bonds, and actually little is known about them.

3–7 LATTICE DEFECTS—NONSTOICHIOMETRIC COMPOUNDS

Defects in Crystals

So far we have assumed that all crystals were ideal. This is not the case in actual practice. Many types of defects appear during the growing process, but only two will be considered here. These may be classified as absences of pairs of cations and anions, Schottky defects (Figure 3–24a), and displacements from the ordered lattice sites to interstitial positions, Frenkel defects (Figure 3–24b). The displacements may occur in either the cation or anion sites, although cation displacement is more likely to occur because the cation is smaller and therefore more easily fits into an interstitial site than does an anion. Displacements of both cations and anions do not occur simultaneously.

Both Frenkel and Schottky defects may occur in the same crystal. With reference to a perfect crystal, the energy requirement for ion displacement is usually greater than for ion vacancy formation. The displacement defects therefore usually occur in crystals in which the ions have a low coordination number and one of the ions, usually the anion, is easily distorted. These properties are generally associated with compounds in which the covalent character of the bond is high. The absences are more likely to occur in compounds in which the two ions are of similar size, not easily distorted and of high coordination number. Compounds of the NaCl type fit this description.

Nonstoichiometric Compounds Defects of the absence and displacement type can be used to account for the nonstoichiometric nature of the oxides, sulfides, nitrides, hydrides, carbides, and some halides of the transitional elements. It should be recognized that the defects which lead to nonstoichiometry are in addition to the Frenkel and Schottky defects which result in nonperfect crystals.

Nonstoichiometric compounds fall into several categories, one

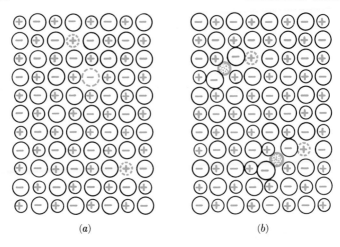

Figure 3–24a Lattice defects. Pairs of cation and
anion vacancies. Schottky defects.

(a)   (b)

Figure 3–24b Interstitial
atoms and lattice vacancy.
Frenkel defects.

of which consists of anion excess and cation deficiencies. This type
is normally found in systems in which the metal can exist in more
than one oxidation state. The iron oxide system for which the
ideal formulas FeO, Fe_3O_4, and Fe_2O_3 are normally written is an example of this class. Iron (II) oxide is actually $Fe_{0.95}O$. The oxide
ions are in cubic closest packing, but only ninety-five out of every
hundred octahedral holes are occupied. Now, if $Fe_{0.95}O$ is oxidized
to Fe_3O_4, the net effect is that oxide layers are added to the lattice
by the reaction $O + 2e \rightarrow O^{-2}$ and that an equivalent number of
iron ions are oxidized $Fe^{2+} \rightarrow Fe^{3+} + e$. The iron ions then
migrate into the holes of the expanded oxygen lattice. This compound has the structure of a spinel in which one-third of the iron
ions are in the (II) state and occupy octahedral holes, and two-
thirds are in the (III) state and are distributed equally between
octahedral and tetrahedral holes. The formula can be written
$Fe_2^{III}Fe^{II}O_4$. Now, if the close-packed oxide ion lattice is further
extended, the next stable composition reached is Fe_2O_3, in which
eight iron (III) ions are distributed between six octahedral and

three tetrahedral sites. Compounds such as these with metal ion deficiencies are semiconductors. There is an electron deficiency, and therefore current flows in this case by the apparent transport of charge through the positive ions, as represented in the equation $M^{2+} \rightarrow M^{3+} + e$. Such compounds are classified as semiconductors of the p type. Further examples of this type are $Fe_{0.86}S$ and $Cu_{1.96}S$.

Another type of deficiency is that due to anion absences. A process may be visualized in which the free nonmetal is evaporated, $O^{2-} \rightarrow O + 2e$, leaving the electrons either trapped in the vacant anion site or located in the vicinity of the cation which has moved to an interstitial site. Titanium oxide, $TiO_{0.69}$, is an example of the former, and ZnO_{1-x} is an example of the latter. In both cases, the excess electrons are free to move under the influence of an applied potential. Such compounds are classified as n type semiconductors. Lattice-defect semiconductors are called intrinsic semiconductors, in contrast to extrinsic semiconductors which result from the introduction of a small number of impurity atoms into the crystal lattice.

IV

Solution Chemistry

THIS CHAPTER is devoted to the reactions of transitional and inner-transitional element ions in water. The questions asked are: How strong an acid is the hydrated cation? At what pH will the hydroxide precipitate? Are the anion and cation stable with respect to oxidation and reduction by water? Are the metal species stable with respect to disproportionation? Is the metal species in solution stable with respect to oxidation by dissolved oxygen? To what extent do the anion and cation interact to form ion pairs? These questions are discussed using the principles of ionic equilibria and standard electrode potentials. The conventions used in the application of the electrode potentials, net equations, and equilibrium quotients are discussed in the Appendix.

4–1 THE ACID PROPERTIES OF CATIONS

An acid will be defined as a substance which yields a proton in solution. Cations qualify as acids because they are capable of reacting with water to produce protons. For instance, when iron (III) perchlorate is dissolved in water, the hydrogen ion concentration of the solution is higher than that of pure water. This is the result of the following reaction:

$$Fe(H_2O)_6^{3+} + H_2O \rightleftarrows Fe(OH)(H_2O)_5^{2+} + H_3O^+$$

(In general, reactions with water are called hydrolysis reactions.) The extent to which this process occurs is measured by the magnitude of the equilibrium quotient for the reaction, which in general terms is:

$$K_{eq} = \frac{[M(OH)(H_2O)^{n-1}][H_3O^+]}{[M(H_2O)_y{}^{n+}]} \qquad (4\text{-}1)$$

Therefore, a comparison of the constants for different metal ions can be used to measure their ability to behave as acids. In comparing the acid behavior of cations, it is convenient first to determine the effect of ion size on equilibrium quotients for ions with similar electron configurations and with the same net charge. The lanthanide ions meet these requirements nicely because they have the same oxidation state, diminish gradually in size, and have similar electron configurations. In Table 4–1 are listed equilibrium quotients for the general reaction described by equation 4–1. Also included is the pH of 0.001 M solutions of the sulfates of these elements.

The general trend for this set of ions of constant charge is to

Table 4–1

Equilibrium Quotients for the Hydrolysis of the M³⁺ Ions of the 4f Electron Elements and La³⁺, and Y³⁺

Cation	Ion Size A	$k \times 10^9$	pH
La³⁺	1.14	0.1	6.45
Ce³⁺	1.034	1.0	5.99
Pr³⁺	1.013	1.0	6.01
Nd³⁺	0.995	0.9	6.02
Sm³⁺	0.964	1.2	5.97
Eu³⁺	0.950	1.3	5.95
Gd³⁺	0.938	1.3	5.95
Y³⁺	0.92	2.0	5.85
Yb³⁺	0.858	3.6	5.72

Table 4–2

**Equilibrium Quotients for the Hydrolysis of
Two Cations of the Same Element in
Different Oxidation States**

Cation	Ion Size A	k
Ce^{3+}	1.034	1×10^{-9}
Ce^{4+}	0.91	0.72
Fe^{2+}	0.85	3×10^{-10}
Fe^{3+}	0.628	2.5×10^{-3}
Co^{2+}	0.80	5×10^{-10}
Co^{3+}	0.56	1.6×10^{-5}
Pu^{3+}	1.00	1.1×10^{-7}
Pu^{4+}	0.86	4×10^{-2}

stronger acid properties as the ion size diminishes. Here, of course, the assumption is that the radii of the hydrated ions vary in the same manner as the crystal ionic radii. One can conclude that, all other factors being equal, the acid property of a cation varies inversely with ion size.

A much greater effect is noted for cations of the same element in two different oxidation states. In fact, the difference in magnitude of the equilibrium quotients for two ions of the same element is so large (Table 4–2) that another factor must be involved: This is the charge on the ion. Both the charge and size are incorporated in the concept called charge density, which in effect is the ratio of charge to the volume of the ion. Ions with high charge density have a greater tendency than ions with small charge densities to retain a hydroxyl group of a water molecule and split out a proton.

Comparison of the equilibrium quotients for the hydrolysis of the M^{3+} ions of the $3d$ transitional elements, for which the charge density varies only slightly and irregularly (Table 4–3), illustrates that still other factors are involved in determining the acid strength of hydrated metal ions. The other factors contributing to the acid properties are not clearly defined, although the effect of the ligand

Table 4–3

Cation	Size A	K_1	Cation	Size A	K_1
Sc^{3+}	0.686	1.26×10^{-6}	Mn^{2+}	0.90	2.5×10^{-11}
Ti^{3+}	0.633	2.0×10^{-2}	Fe^{2+}	0.85	3.1×10^{-10}
V^{3+}	0.625	2.0×10^{-3}	Co^{2+}	0.80	5×10^{-10}
Cr^{3+}	0.608	1.02×10^{-5}	Ni^{2+}	0.76	5×10^{-9}
Fe^{3+}	0.628	2.5×10^{-3}	Cu^{2+}	0.80	1.58×10^{-7}
Co^{3+}	0.56	1.6×10^{-5}	Zn^{2+}	0.83	1.5×10^{-10}

field on the splitting of the d orbitals and the order of electron filling is probably involved. This points up the fact that the application of charge density as a means of predicting acid properties of
cations must be used cautiously. Part of the problem, however, is
that it is very difficult to assemble data all of which have been run
under similar conditions. Most of the data reported in this section
were obtained at 25°, but under varying salt concentrations.

Actually the acid properties of the metal cation cannot be ade-
quately described by one simple equation. The hydrolysis reaction
may proceed further, and indeed the OH and O groups may act as
bridges between metal ions in the formation of polymeric metal
species. The net equations which illustrate other possible reactions follow below. (The metal ions are hydrated, but to simplify
the equations, the waters of hydration are not shown.)

$$M(OH)^{n-1} + H_2O \rightleftarrows M(OH)_2^{n-2} + H_3O^+$$
$$M(OH)_2^{n-2} + H_2O \rightleftarrows M(OH)_3^{n-3} + H_3O^+$$
$$2M^{n+} + 2H_2O \rightleftarrows M_2(OH)^{2n-1} + H_3O^+$$
$$2M^{n+} + 4H_2O \rightleftarrows M_2(OH)_2^{2n-2} + 2H_3O^+$$
$$3M^{n+} + 16H_2O \rightleftarrows M_3(OH)_8^{3n-8} + 8H_3O^+$$
$$4M^{n+} + 16H_2O \rightleftarrows M_4(OH)_8^{4n-8} + 8H_3O^+$$

The concentration of these species in a given solution depends
upon the particular element present, the magnitude of the equilibrium constants, and the initial concentrations of metal ion and
hydrogen ion. Hydrogen ion is a product species in each of these
reactions, and therefore some control over the composition of the

Table 4-4
Percent Zirconium Polymer in Solution as a Function of Metal Ion and Hydrogen Ion Concentration

	Zr Conc. mM/liter	Percent polymer
2 M H^+	3.9	29
	6.3	42
	12.4	59
1 M H^+	0.32	6
	1.00	36
	3.2	66

metal species may be exercised by adjusting the hydrogen ion concentration. Thus, the equilibrium concentration of hydrolyzed species can be reduced by increasing the hydrogen-ion concentration; conversely, a higher concentration of hydrolyzed species can be obtained by decreasing the hydrogen ion concentration. Similarly, an increase in metal ion concentration favors the formation of polymeric species. The data in Table 4-4 are illustrative of this principle.

Polymeric species are most likely to be found in solutions with ions of high-charge densities. All the $M(IV)$ ions form polymeric species even at relatively low metal ion concentrations. The major species in the zirconium and hafnium solutions seem to be of the type $Zr_4(OH)_8^{8+}$, and $Zr_3(OH)_6^{6+}$. Cerium and thorium form species such as $Ce_2(OH)_4^{4+}$, and $Th_2(OH)_2^{6+}$. Even in solutions of trivalent ions there is evidence for ions such as $Sc_2(OH)_2^{4+}$, and $La_2(OH)^{5+}$. Many of these reactions reach equilibrium slowly, and therefore solutions prepared at different times may not contain equilibrium concentrations of the expected species. Thus, the history of the solution may well have a bearing on the experimental observations made on the properties of these solutions.

No data have been given for the other $4d$ and $5d$ transitional elements simply because they do not exhibit this kind of chemistry.

The niobium, tantalum, molybdenum, and tungsten oxides in their highest oxidation states are all insoluble in water, and their anhydrous halides react with water to precipitate the oxides. At high hydrogen ion concentrations, these oxides do dissolve to a limited extent to yield VO_2^+, MoO^{3+}, VO^{2+}, MoO_2^{2+}, WO_2^{2+} ions in solution. These oxygenated cations

$$V_2O_{5(s)} + 2H^+ \rightleftarrows 2VO_2^+ + H_2O$$

are acids, because in the reverse reaction a proton is a product species.

Uranium, neptunium, plutonium, and americium form the interesting ions MO_2^{2+} and MO_2^+ in solution. Salts of these cations can be recovered from solution. The UO_2^{2+} has been shown to be linear, and presumably the other ions have the same structure because they can be substituted for the uranyl ion in the solid state.

4–2 HYDROXIDE PRECIPITATION

The ultimate result of hydrolysis is the formation of the neutral hydroxylated species. All the hydroxides of the transitional elements are insoluble in water. If the composition of the hydroxide and the composition of the species in equilibrium with the hydroxide are known, then the solubility product can be calculated from the solubility data. The net equation for the equilibrium is written as

$$M(OH)_n \rightleftarrows M^{n+} + nOH^-$$

for which the solubility product is

$$K_{sp} = [M^{n+}][OH^-]^n \qquad (4\text{–}2)$$

The maximum pH to which a solution may be raised before precipitation occurs is determined by the magnitude of the solubility product and the metal ion concentration. This "pH of precipitation" is of practical importance as it determines the latitude the experimenter has in varying the pH of a solution without encountering a hydroxide precipitate. It may be calculated by substituting for OH^- in Equation 4–2 its equivalent $K_w/[H^+]$ to give,

$$K_{sp} = [M^{n+}]\left(\frac{K_w}{[H^+]}\right)^n \qquad (4\text{--}3)$$

Upon taking the logarithm of this equation, substituting pH for $\log 1/[H^+]$, and rearranging, the following expression results:

$$pH = \frac{1}{n} \log K_{sp} - \frac{1}{n} \log [M^{n+}] - \log K_w \qquad (4\text{--}4)$$

Here n is the charge on the cation in equilibrium with the solid, and K_w is the ion product of water.

As with the hydrolysis constants, the magnitude of the hydroxide solubility product for a series of ions of the same electron configuration and charge decreases with increasing size of the cation. Again, this relationship appears to hold only when all the other factors affecting the solubility are essentially constant, thus allowing the effect of size to be seen. The solubility products of the inner-transitional element hydroxides allow a suitable comparison (Table 4–5). The pH of precipitation is calculated for 0.001 M solutions. The data for scandium, yttrium, and lantha-

Table 4–5

Solubility Products and pH of Precipitation for 0.001 M Lanthanide Perchlorate Solutions, Sc^{3+}, Y^{3+}, and La^{3+}

Cation	K_{sp}	pH pptn.	Cation	K_{sp}	pH pptn.
Sc^{3+}	1.3×10^{-31}	4.7	Eu^{3+}	0.9×10^{-23}	7.4
Y^{3+}	6.2×10^{-23}	7.6	Gd^{3+}	1.8×10^{-23}	7.6
La^{3+}	1.7×10^{-19}	8.8	Er^{3+}	4.1×10^{-24}	7.2
Ce^{3+}	1.6×10^{-21}	8.1	Tm^{3+}	3.2×10^{-24}	7.0
Pr^{3+}	6.7×10^{-22}	8.0	Yb^{3+}	3.2×10^{-24}	7.0
Nd^{3+}	3.2×10^{-22}	7.9	Lu^{3+}	6.5×10^{-24}	7.2
Sm^{3+}	8.4×10^{-23}	7.7			

num are included for comparison. Keep in mind that only solubility products of the same form can be compared.

By contrast, hydroxides of ions with a higher charge density such as Ti(IV), Zr(IV), Hf(IV), and Th(IV) precipitate from a 0.001 M solution at a pH of 1.5, 2.05, 2.13, and 3.5 respectively. Other oxidation-state-four ions also precipitate at a low pH, and in general there is much less latitude in the pH range over which these solutions may be varied as compared to solutions of ions of lower charge densities.

The M^{2+} and M^{3+} ions of the $3d$ transitional elements also form insoluble hydroxides, with the hydroxide of the higher oxidation state being less soluble than the hydroxide of oxidation state (II), (Table 4–6). The pH of precipitation is calculated for 0.001 M solutions.

A few of the hydroxides dissolve in strong bases to give anionic species. These hydroxides are said to be amphoteric. The net equation is

$$Cr(OH)_3 + OH^- \rightleftarrows Cr(OH)_4^-$$

In addition to chromium hydroxide, the hydroxides of scandium and vanadium (IV) are also amphoteric.

Table 4–6

Solubility Products and pH of Precipitation for Ions of the $3d$ Transitional Elements (0.001 M)

Cation	K_{sp}	pH pptn.	Cation	K_{sp}	pH pptn.
Cr^{2+}	1×10^{-17}	7.0	Cr^{3+}	6.7×10^{-31}	5.0
Mn^{2+}	1×10^{-14}	8.5			
Fe^{2+}	1×10^{-14}	8.5	Fe^{3+}	1×10^{-38}	2.4
Co^{2+}	1×10^{-14}	8.5	Co^{3+}	4×10^{-26}	6.5
Ni^{2+}	3.2×10^{-14}	8.75			
Cu^{2+}	5.0×10^{-19}	6.0			

4–3   OXYANION SPECIES

Monomeric Anions

Those transitional elements which exhibit the oxidation states five and higher form anionic species. Vanadium, niobium, and tantalum have the maximum oxidation state of five in the anions VO_3^-, VO_4^{3-}, NbO_4^{3-}, and TaO_4^{3-}. The alkali metavanadates are slightly soluble, but the niobates and tantalates are insoluble and are formed in fused systems only. The oxides are insoluble in water and are not considered to be acid anhydrides.

Chromium, molybdenum, and tungsten have a maximum oxidation state of six, and all form soluble alkali metal salts of the CrO_4^{2-}, MoO_4^{2-}, and WO_4^{2-} anions. The acids H_2MoO_4 and H_2WO_4 are insoluble. H_2CrO_4 is not isolable, and only CrO_3 is recovered from solution. A solution of CrO_3 is a strong acid:

$$CrO_3 + H_2O \rightarrow H_2CrO_4$$
$$H_2CrO_4 \rightleftarrows H^+ + HCrO_4^-$$

Manganese, technetium, and rhenium in the oxidation state seven form the anions MnO_4^-, TcO_4^-, and ReO_4^-. The acids $HReO_4$ and $HTcO_4$ can be isolated from solution, but $HMnO_4$ exists only in solution. They are all strong acids. The oxidation-state-six anions may also be prepared, although they are unstable with respect to disproportionation to the VII and IV states. Manganese anions MnO_3^{2-} and MnO_4^{3-} can be prepared by the oxidation of MnO_2 in a fused system.

Osmium and ruthenium form oxides OsO_4 and RuO_4 in the oxidation state eight, but iron does not. These oxides, although expected to be anhydrides of strong acids, actually have very weak acid properties. The oxidation states six and seven in MO_4^{2-} and MO_4^- can be achieved by the oxidation of the metal in a fused system. Iron forms an insoluble ferrate $BaFeO_4$ by electrolytic oxidation in aqueous solution. The remaining transitional elements do not exhibit oxyanion formation in aqueous solution. All the ions of composition MO_4^{8-n} are tetrahedral in structure. It is probable that hybridized d^3s orbitals are used to accommodate the electron-pair bonds.

Isopoly Anions

An interesting property of the Group V and Group VI anions is that they condense to form polymeric anionic species with an increase in the hydrogen ion concentration of the solution.

$$3HVO_4^{2-} + 3H^+ \rightleftarrows V_3O_9^{3-} + 3H_2O$$
$$2HCrO_4^- + H^+ \rightleftarrows Cr_2O_7^{2-} + 2H_2O$$
$$6WO_4^{2-} + 7H^+ \rightleftarrows HW_6O_{21}^{5-} + 3H_2O$$

Polymeric anions resulting from the condensation of one kind of monomer are called isopoly anions. In the case of vanadium and chromium, the polymers form by sharing of the corners of VO_4^{3-} and CrO_4^{2-} tetrahedra. In the case of the others, the polymerization must occur initially through the condensation of MO_4^{2-} tetrahedra and, finally, through the joining of MO_6 octahedra through corners and edges. The end result of the polymerization is the precipitation of the neutral oxide. It should be noted that in the formation of polymeric anions, the extent of polymerization increases with an increase in hydrogen ion concentration. This is in contrast to the polymerization of cations in which the reverse is true. By comparing the net equations, it can be seen that in the case of the anion, water is split out as a product, while in that of the cation, water is a reactant.

$$4Zr^{4+} + 8H_2O \rightleftarrows Zr_4(OH)_8^{8+} + 8H^+$$
$$7MoO_4^{2-} + 8H^+ \rightleftarrows Mo_7O_{24}^{6-} + 4H_2O$$

The composition of the products crystallized from these solutions depends upon the pH of the solution. The paramolybdate $(NH_4)_6Mo_7O_{24}\cdot 4H_2O$ and paratungstate $Na_5(HW_6O_{21})$ are obtained from near-neutral solutions.

Heteropoly Anions

Solutions of vanadates, molybdates, or tungstates, when acidified in the presence of another ionic species (usually an anion such as phosphate), yield a new complex anion containing both elements in a polymeric structure. Polymeric anions which contain two kinds of elements other than oxygen are called heteropoly anions.

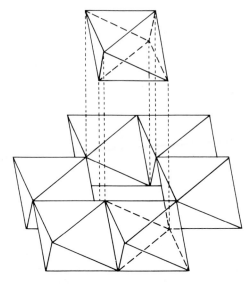

Figure 4–1   Structure of a six-heteropoly acid with the central octahedron raised to show the annular arrangement of the six MoO$_6$ octahedra.

In the specific case of molybdate and phosphate, the end product is $(PMo_{12}O_{21}^{6-})$. There are two main classes of heteropoly anions, grouped according to the number of molybdenum or tungsten atoms in the complex. These are the twelve-anions, and the six-anions. There are intermediate classes, but these will not be considered here. Compounds of the twelve-heteropoly anions have the general formula $H_{8-n}(XM_{12}O_{40})$, where M is molybdenum or tungsten and X may be Si, B, As, P, Te, Ti, Ge, Sn, Zr, Hf, Th, and Ge. Compounds of the six-heteropoly anions have the general formula $H_{12-n}(XM_6O_{24})$ where M is molybdenum or tungsten, and X may be I, Te, Fe, Al, Co, Ni, Rh, Cu, or Mn.

The structures of the six and twelve anions are given in Figures 4–1 and 4–2, respectively. Each is constituted of MO$_6$ groups. In the six class, six of the MO$_6$ octahedra share edges to form an annular ring with the void in the center available for occupancy by an atom of the second element. When the center is occupied by an

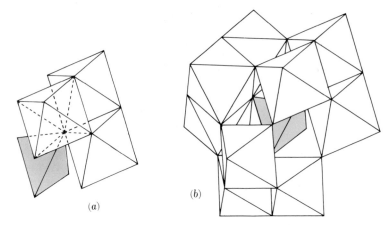

Figure 4–2 Structure of a twelve-heteropoly acid $[RW_{12}O_{40}]^{3-}$. (a) Grouping of three WO_6 octahedra sharing an oxygen with a PO_4 tetrahedron. (b) Figure showing how four groups of three WO_6 octahedra share corners to surround the PO_4 tetrahedron in a cage.

atom of the same element, the anion is classed as an isopoly anion; when occupied by a different element, a heteropoly anion. The paratungstate referred to previously is really a heteropoly anion, because the central position is occupied by hydrogen. In the twelve series, three MO_6 octahedra share three corner oxygens and one apical oxygen to form Mo_3O_{13} units, which in turn share corners with adjacent Mo_3O_{13} units to form a cagelike structure. The four apical oxygens projecting into the cage form a tetrahedron around the atom of the second element. It is interesting to note that the acids of these anions can in general be extracted into an organic solvent such as diethyl ether.

4–4 CATION-ANION ION ASSOCIATION

The reaction of the hydrated cation with water to give hydroxylated ions was dealt with in Section 4–1. This is not the only such reaction to be considered, however, for the cation may also be involved in an equilibrium with the anion of the salt:

$$M(H_2O)_6^{n+} + X^- \rightleftarrows MX(H_2O)_5^{(n-1)} + H_2O$$

Therefore the major species in solution depends upon the kind of equilibrium established in solution, the concentrations of the individual species, and the magnitude of the equilibrium constants. To illustrate, consider what happens when the salts, iron (III) chloride, and iron (III) nitrate are dissolved in water. The iron (III) chloride solution is yellow, and the iron (III) nitrate solution is yellow-brown. The addition of nitric acid to both results in essentially no change in the chloride solution, but it results in a colorless solution in the nitrate case. These observations can be accounted for by the following net equations:

$$Fe(H_2O)_6^{3+} + Cl^- \rightleftarrows FeCl(H_2O)_5^{2+} + H_2O$$
$$Fe(H_2O)_6^{3+} + H_2O \rightleftarrows Fe(OH)(H_2O)_5^{2+} + H_3O^+$$

The chloro complex is yellow, the hydroxo complex yellow-brown, and the hydrated iron ion is colorless. The hydrolysis equilibrium is hydrogen ion dependent, and the chloro complex equilibrium is not. Therefore, as the hydrogen-ion concentration is increased, equilibrium concentrations are readjusted so that the concentration of the hydroxylated species is decreased and the concentration of the hydrated species is increased. The nitrate ion is a poor complexing ion compared to the chloride ion and is not involved in the equilibrium. Of course, $FeCl_2^{2+}$, $FeCl_3$, and $FeCl_4^-$ must also be considered. The concentration of each depends upon the chloride concentration and the magnitude of the equilibrium constants. The equilibrium constant for the formation of $FeCl^{2+}$ is 32, and a simple calculation shows that the Fe^{3+} and $FeCl^{2+}$ concentrations are equal at a chloride concentration of about 0.03M. These data show that the nature of the salt dissolved in water has a great effect on the nature of the species actually in solution.

Association of the transitional element ions with fluoride ion is particularly strong, except for the ions of the platinum group. Note the large positive values for the first equilibrium constant (Table 4–7). A calculation based on the K_1^* for the zirconium complex shows that at 1 M H^+ and 1×10^{-8} M HF, nine out of

Table 4-7

Log of Equilibrium Quotients† for the Complex Ions of the Transitional and Inner-Transitional Elements

Cation	*F$^-$	Cl$^-$	Br$^-$	I$^-$	NO$_3^-$
		log K_1			
Fe^{2+}	<1.5	0.36	—	—	—
Co^{2+}	—	− 2.40	—	—	—
Ni^{2+}	0.16	—	—	—	—
Sc^{3+}	6.19	—	—	—	—
Y^{3+}	—	2.3	2.8	—	—
La^{3+}	2.68	− 0.15	—	—	—
Ce^{3+}	3.11	$\sim$ 0.1	0.38	—	$\sim$ 0.40
Gd^{3+}	3.37	—	—	—	—
Cr^{3+}	4.36	− 0.65	—	—	—
Fe^{3+}	5.21	1.48	0.60	—	—
Ce^{4+}	3.11	—	—	—	—
Zr^{4+}	8.71	0.92	—	—	0.3
Th^{4+}	7.56	0.11	—	—	− 0.3
U^{4+}	$\geqslant$ 8.91	0.26	0.18	—	0.46
Pd^{2+}	noev.	6.1	—	—	—
Pt^{2+}	for complex	—	—	—	—
Zn^{2+}	—	0.6	0.22	<−1	—
Cd^{2+}	—	2.00	1.56	2.28	—
Hg^{2+}	—	6.74	8.94	3.71	—

* HF is a weak acid and therefore this constant is for the equilibrium

$$HF + M^{n+} \rightleftarrows MF^{n-1} + H^+$$

† J. Byerrum, G. Schwarzenbach, and L. G. Sillen, eds; *Stability Constants of Metal-Ion Complexes;* Part II, "Inorganic Ligands" (London Chemical Society, 1957).

ten zirconium ions in solution are ZrF$^+$ species. For metal ions at the beginning of the transitional series, the order of complexing is F$^-$ > Cl$^-$ $\geqslant$ Br$^-$ > I$^-$. This is generally supported by the data in Table 4–8, although there are some instances in which the chlo-

Table 4–8
Standard Electrode Potentials

3d period	$-E°$	4d period	$-E°$	5d period	$-E°$	4f period	$-E°$	6d period	$-E°$
$Sc^{3+} + 3e \rightleftarrows Sc$	2.08	$Y^{3+} + 3e \rightleftarrows Y$	2.37	$La^{3+} + 3e \rightleftarrows La$	2.52	$Ce^{3+} + 3e \rightleftarrows Ce$	2.48	$Ac^{3+} + 3e \rightleftarrows Ac$	2.60
$Ti^{3+} + 3e \rightleftarrows Ti$	1.63	$Zr^{4+} + 4e \rightleftarrows Zr$	1.56	$Hf^{4+} + 4e \rightleftarrows Hf$	1.70	$Pr^{3+} + 3e \rightleftarrows Pr$	2.47	$Th^{4+} + 4e \rightleftarrows Th$	1.90
$V^{3+} + 3e \rightleftarrows V$	0.87	$Nb^{3+} + 3e \rightleftarrows Nb$	~1.1	$Ta_2O_5 + 10H^+ + 10e \rightleftarrows 2Ta + 5H_2O$	0.81			5f period	
$Cr^{3+} + 3e \rightleftarrows Cr$	0.74	$Mo^{3+} + 3e \rightleftarrows Mo$	~0.2	$W^{3+} + 3e \rightleftarrows W$	$\simeq 0.11$	$Nd^{3+} + 3e \rightleftarrows Nd$	2.44	$U^{3+} + 3e \rightleftarrows U$	1.80
$Mn^{2+} + 2e \rightleftarrows Mn$	1.18	$Tc^{3+} + 2e \rightleftarrows Tc$	$\simeq 0.24$	$ReO_2 + 4H^+ + 4e \rightleftarrows Re + 2H_2O$	-0.252	$Pm^{3+} + 3e \rightleftarrows Pm$	2.42	$Np^{3+} + 3e \rightleftarrows Np$	1.83
						$Sm^{3+} + 3e \rightleftarrows Sm$	2.41	$Pu^{3+} + 3e \rightleftarrows Pu$	2.03
$Fe^{2+} + 2e \rightleftarrows Fe$	0.440	$Ru^{2+} + 2e \rightleftarrows Ru$	$\simeq 0.4$	$OsO_4 + 8H^+ + 8e \rightleftarrows Os + 4H_2O$	-0.85	$Eu^{3+} + 3e \rightleftarrows Eu$	2.41	$Am^{3+} + 3e \rightleftarrows Am$	2.38
						$Gd^{3+} + 3e \rightleftarrows Gd$	2.40	$Cm^{3+} + 3e \rightleftarrows Cm$	2.38
$Co^{2+} + 2e \rightleftarrows Co$	0.277	$Rh^{3+} + 3e \rightleftarrows Rh$	$\simeq 0.8$	$Ir^{3+} + 3e \rightleftarrows Ir$	$\simeq 1.15$	$Tb^{3+} + 3e \rightleftarrows Tb$	2.39		
$Ni^{2+} + 2e \rightleftarrows Ni$	0.250	$Pd^{2+} + 2e \rightleftarrows Pd$	-0.987	$Pt^{2+} + 2e \rightleftarrows Pt$	$\simeq 1.2$	$Dy^{3+} + 3e \rightleftarrows Dy$	2.35		
$Cu^{2+} + 2e \rightleftarrows Cu$	-0.337	$Ag^{1+} + 1e \rightleftarrows Ag$	-0.799	$Au^{3+} + 3e \rightleftarrows Au$	-1.50	$Ho^{3+} + 3e \rightleftarrows Ho$	2.32		
						$Er^{3+} + 3e \rightleftarrows Er$	2.30		
						$Tm^{3+} + 3e \rightleftarrows Tm$	2.28		
						$Yb^{3+} + 3e \rightleftarrows Yb$	2.27		
						$Lu^{3+} + 3e \rightleftarrows Lu$	2.25		

ride and bromide are reversed. Also included in the Table for comparison are data for cadmium and mercury, for which the iodide has a large value and the fluoride value is too small to determine. Along with nitrate, the perchlorate ion is considered to have a very low tendency to associate with cations. Therefore, perchlorate salts are generally used under conditions in which the anion-cation association is to be held to a minimum.

4–5   OXIDATION-REDUCTION REACTIONS

Water is so commonly used as a solvent that its chemical properties are sometimes overlooked. In addition to being involved in acid-base chemistry, water also has an important oxidation-reduction chemistry. These reactions will be discussed in terms of electrode potentials, a brief development of which will be found in the Appendix. The two reactions which are related to water as an oxidizing or reducing agent are:

In acid solution

$$2H^+ + 2e \rightarrow H_2 \qquad\qquad E^\circ = 0.00$$
$$O_2 + 4H^+ + 4e \rightarrow 2H_2O \qquad E^\circ = 1.23$$

In basic solution

$$2H_2O + 2e \rightarrow H_2 + 2OH^- \qquad\qquad E_B^\circ = -0.826$$
$$O_2 + 2H_2O + 4e \rightarrow 4OH^- \qquad\qquad E_B^\circ = 0.404$$

The electrode potentials are referred to the standard conditions of an ideal one molal solution of ions and one atmosphere gaseous pressure. The manner in which these potentials change with pH is shown in Figure 4–3. As the hydrogen-ion concentration decreases (pH goes to higher values), a stronger reducing agent is required to reduce hydrogen ion to hydrogen gas. Similarly, as the hydrogen-ion concentration decreases, water is more easily oxidized to oxygen gas. Any half-reaction with a potential between the two lines is stable with respect to oxidation or reduction by water. However, the reduced species of the half-reaction is unstable with respect to oxidation by oxygen gas, and the oxidized species of the half-reaction is unstable with respect to reduction by hydro-

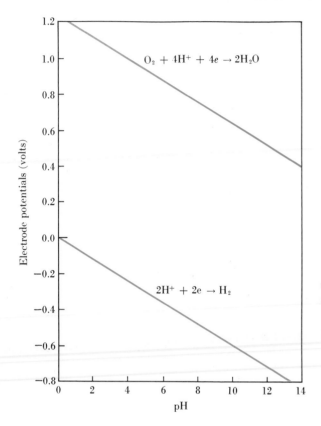

Figure 4–3   Change in E values for the $2H^+ + 2e \rightarrow H_2$ couple and $O_2 + 4H^+ + 4e \rightarrow 2H_2O$ couple as a function of pH.

gen gas. These gas reactions involve steps which are slow, and very often these reactions do not proceed unless a catalyst is present. The half-reactions which do not contain H^+, OH^-, or water as reactants or products are not affected by changes in the hydrogen-ion concentration. All other half-reactions are dependent upon the H^+ concentration, and the $E°$ must be corrected for nonstandard conditions. The change in pH may also affect competing reactions, such as the precipitation of a hydroxide, and this must be kept in mind when predicting what kind of reaction will occur.

Metals as Reducing Agents

The standard electrode potentials for the metals of the transitional and inner-transitional elements are listed in Table 4–8. Note that most of the metals are strong enough reducing agents to be oxidized by water or hydrogen ion. In the $3d$ series, only copper requires an oxidizing agent stronger than hydrogen ion. The potentials in the $4d$ and $5d$ series fall off rapidly across the period, and by the time technetium and tungsten are reached, oxidizing agents stronger than hydrogen ion are required for the solution of these metals. The $4f$ and $5f$ elements are very strong reducing agents.

In actual practice, the reactivity of the metal depends upon the tenacity of the oxide film formed on the surface of the metal. Elements such as titanium, zirconium, and hafnium are actually inert at room temperature because of the protective oxide, although they would be expected to react with water on the basis of their high negative potential.

Cycle calculations of the type used in Section 2–5 can be used to explain the difference in nickel and palladium as reducing agents. The energy change for the reaction

$$M_{(s)} + \frac{n}{2} H_{(aq)}^{+} \rightleftarrows M_{(aq)}^{+n} + \frac{n}{2} H_{2(g)}$$

is a measure of the extent to which this reaction will go. However, because the hydrogen gas-hydrogen ion part of the cycle is common to both reactions, it is not necessary to include this half-reaction for the purpose of comparison. The net equation can be broken into its component parts as follows:

	kcal/mole			kcal/mole
$Ni_{(s)} \rightarrow Ni_{(g)}$	+87.4	Sublimation energy	$Pd_{(s)} \rightarrow Pd_{(g)}$	+101.0
$Ni_{(g)} \rightarrow Ni_{(g)}^{2+} + 2e$	+418.5	Ionization potential	$Pd_{(g)} \rightarrow Pd_{(g)}^{2+} + 2e$	+447.8
$q + Ni_{(g)}^{2+} \rightarrow Ni_{(aq)}^{2+}$	−527.4	Hydration energy	$aq + Pd_{(g)}^{2+} \rightarrow Pd_{(aq)}^{2+}$	−510.5
	−11.5			+38.3

The combination of higher sublimation energy and ionization potential and a lower heat of hydration for palladium results in palladium being a poorer reducing agent than nickel. Looking at it in a different way, a stronger oxidizing agent is required to put palladium into solution than is required for nickel. Similar comparisons can be made for the other elements.

Oxidation-Reduction Chemistry of the Ions. The standard electrode potentials for half-reactions of the ions are tabulated in Table 4–9.

The Group III elements scandium, yttrium, and lanthanum only have the oxidation state III in aqueous solution. These ions have a rare gas configuration and would not be expected to show a higher oxidation state, although a lower oxidation state might be attained especially in a nonaqueous solvent.

Titanium (III) is a moderately good reducing agent. It is stable in water with respect to oxidation by water, but it is easily oxidized by oxygen at all pH's. Titanium (II) will reduce hydrogen ion at all pH's below about 6 and is easily oxidized by oxygen of the air. The potentials for the reduced states of zirconium, hafnium, and thorium are not given, but all are unstable with respect to oxidation by water and oxygen.

Vanadium (II) is stable in water to about pH 4; below this it will reduce hydrogen ion to hydrogen gas. It is also unstable with respect to oxidation by oxygen of the air. Vanadium (III) is a stable species in water with respect to reduction, although a mild oxidizing agent will take it to the four state. VO_2^+ is a good oxidizing agent and is stable in water with respect to reduction by water. The potentials for niobium in both the oxidation states IV and III make them good enough reducing agents to take hydrogen ion to hydrogen at pH's below six. Therefore their aqueous chemistry is limited. Actually, at this pH an insoluble hydroxide would probably precipitate. Although values are not given for tantalum, its reduced states are even better reducing agents. As a consequence, the oxidation-state-five species for niobium and tantalum are poor oxidizing agents compared to vanadium (V).

Chromium in the oxidation state (VI) is a strong oxidizing

Table 4–9
Standard Electrode Potentials* 25° 1m H⁺

Half-reactions	$E°$
$Ti^{3+} + 1e \rightarrow Ti^{2+}$	-0.37
$Ti(IV) + 1e \rightarrow Ti^{3+}$	$+0.20$
$V^{3+} + 1e \rightarrow V^{2+}$	$+0.255$
$2H^+ + VO^{2+} + 1e \rightarrow V^{3+} + H_2O$	$+0.337$
$2H^+ + VO_2^+ + 1e \rightarrow VO^{2+} + H_2O$	$+1.0$
$Nb(V) + 1e \rightarrow Nb(IV)$	-0.4 HCl solution
$2H^+ + NbO^{3+} + 2e \rightarrow Nb^{3+} + H_2O$	-0.344 HCl solution
$Cr^{3+} + 1e \rightarrow Cr^{2+}$	-0.41
$14H^+ + Cr_2O_7^{2-} + 6e \rightarrow 2Cr^{3+} + 7H_2O$	$+1.33$
$Mo(V) + 2e \rightarrow Mo(III)$	$+0.23$ H_2SO_4 solution
$Mo(IV) + 1e \rightarrow Mo(III)$	$+0.1$ H_2SO_4 solution
$2H^+ + MoO_2^{2+} + 1e \rightarrow MoO^{3+} + H_2O$	$+0.48$ HCl solution
$Mo(CN)_8^{3-} + 1e \rightarrow Mo(CN)_8^{4-}$	$+0.73$
$2H^+ + H_2MoO_4 + 1e \rightarrow MoO_2^+ + 2H_2O$	$+0.4$
$2H^+ + W_2O_5 + 2e \rightarrow 2WO_2 + H_2O$	-0.04
$2H^+ + 2WO_3 + 2e \rightarrow W_2O_5 + H_2O$	-0.03
$W(CN)_8^{3-} + 1e \rightarrow W(CN)_8^{4-}$	$+0.457$
$Mn^{3+} + 1e \rightarrow Mn^{2+}$	$+1.51$
$4H^+ + MnO_2 + 1e \rightarrow Mn^{3+} + 2H_2O$	$+0.95$
$4H^+ + MnO_4^{2-} + 2e \rightarrow MnO_2 + 2H_2O$	$+2.26$
$MnO_4^- + 1e \rightarrow MnO_4^{2-}$	$+0.564$
$4H^+ + MnO_4^- + 3e \rightarrow MnO_2 + 2H_2O$	$+1.695$
$4H^+ + TcO_4^- + 3e \rightarrow TcO_2 + 2H_2O$	$+0.74$
$4H^+ + ReO_4^- + 3e \rightarrow ReO_2 + 2H_2O$	$+0.51$
$4H^+ + TcO_2 + 2e \rightarrow Tc^{2+} + 2H_2O$	$+0.6$
$4H^+ + ReO_2 + 1e \rightarrow Re^{3+} + 2H_2O$	$+0.2$
$Fe^{3+} + 1e \rightarrow Fe^{2+}$	$+0.771$
$Co^{3+} + 1e \rightarrow Co^{2+}$	$+1.84$
$Co(NH_3)_6^{3+} + 1e \rightarrow Co(NH_3)_6^{2+}$	$+0.10$
$RuO_4 + 1e \rightarrow RuO_4^-$	$+1.00$
$RuO_4^- + 1e \rightarrow RuO_4^{2-}$	$+0.59$
$Ru(IV)Cl_x + 1e \rightarrow Ru(III)Cl_x$	$+0.86$
$Ru(III)Cl_x + 1e \rightarrow Ru(II)Cl_x$	$+0.08$
$4H^+ + OsO_4 + 4e \rightarrow OsO_2 + 2H_2O$	$+0.96$
$OsCl_6^{2-} + 1e \rightarrow OsCl_6^{3-}$	$+0.85$
$Rh(VI) + 2e \rightarrow Rh(IV)$	$+1.5$

Table 4-9 (*continued*)

Half-reactions	$E°$
$Rh(IV) + 1e \rightarrow Rh(III)$	$+1.43$
$IrCl_6^{2-} + 1e \rightarrow IrCl_6^{3-}$	$+1.02$
$4H^+ + IrO_2 + 1e \rightarrow Ir^{3+} + 2H_2O$	$+0.7$
$PdCl_6^{2-} + 2e \rightarrow PdCl_4^{2-} + 2Cl^-$	$+1.29$
$PtCl_6^{2-} + 2e \rightarrow PtCl_4^{2-} + 2Cl^-$	$+0.74$
$Cu^{2+} + 1e \rightarrow Cu^+$	$+0.153$
$Ag^{2+} + 1e \rightarrow Ag^+$	$+2.00$
$AuCl_4^- + 2e \rightarrow AuCl_2 + 2Cl^-$	$+0.93$
$Eu^{3+} + 1e \rightarrow Eu^{2+}$	-0.43
$Sm^{3+} + 1e \rightarrow Sm^{2+}$	-1.55
$Yb^{3+} + 1e \rightarrow Yb^{2+}$	-1.15
$Ce(IV) + 1e \rightarrow Ce^{3+}$	$+1.70$
$U^{4+} + 1e \rightarrow U^{3+}$	-0.63
$Np^{4+} + 1e \rightarrow Np^{3+}$	$+0.15$
$Pu^{4+} + 1e \rightarrow Pu^{3+}$	$+0.98$
$Am^{4+} + 1e \rightarrow Am^{3+}$	$+2.44$
$Bk^{4+} + 1e \rightarrow Bk^{3+}$	$+1.70$
$UO_2^+ + 4H^+ + 1e \rightarrow U^{4+} + 2H_2O$	$+0.55$
$NpO_2^+ + 4H^+ + 1e \rightarrow Np^{4+} + 2H_2O$	$+0.74$
$PuO_2^+ + 4H^+ + 1e \rightarrow Pu^{4+} + 2H_2O$	$+1.15$
$AmO_2^+ + 4H^+ + 1e \rightarrow Am^{4+} + 2H_2O$	$+1.60$
$UO_2^{2+} + 1e \rightarrow UO_2^+$	$+0.06$
$NpO_2^{2+} + 1e \rightarrow NpO_2^+$	$+1.14$
$PuO_2^{2+} + 1e \rightarrow PuO_2^+$	$+0.916$
$AmO_2^{2+} + 1e \rightarrow AmO_2^+$	$+1.60$

Taken in part from G. Charlot, *Selected Constants—Oxidation Reduction Potentials* (London: Pergamon Press, 1958) and W. Latimer, *Oxidation Potentials* (2nd ed; Englewood Cliffs, N.J. Prentice-Hall, 1952).

* Those ions with the oxidation state designated with a Roman numeral have an uncertain composition.

agent. Note that the $4d$ and $5d$ homologs tungstate and molybdate are relatively poor oxidizing agents. This means that their reduced states are good reducing agents. Most of the reduced states are probably present as some complex ion rather than the hydrated ion.

Chromium (III), however, is stable in water. Chromium (II) will reduce hydrogen ion at concentrations greater than $10^{-6}M$ and will be easily oxidized by oxygen.

Now with Mn(II) we have an ion which is stable in aqueous solution with respect to oxidation by oxygen and water. The potential of $+1.5$ makes manganese (III) a good oxidizing agent, but coupled with the Mn(III)—Mn(IV) half-reaction, it is apparent that manganese (III) is unstable with respect to disproportionation to the II and IV state.

$$2Mn^{3+} + 2H_2O \rightarrow MnO_2 + Mn^{2+} + 4H^+$$

The manganate ion is also a good oxidizing agent, but it is also unstable with respect to disproportionation to the IV and VII state.

$$4H^+ + 3MnO_4^{2-} \rightarrow MnO_2 + 2MnO_4^- + 2H_2O$$

The permanganate ion has a sufficiently high potential to oxidize water, and, in fact, this reaction does proceed very slowly at room temperature.

$$4H^+ + 4MnO_4^- \rightarrow 3O_2 + 4MnO_2 + 2H_2O$$

Note that the pertechnetate and perrhenate ions are much poorer oxidizing agents, continuing the trend of the preceding groups. The reduced states of technetium and rhenium must therefore be better reducing agents than manganese (II) and manganese (IV).

The iron (III) ion is a reasonably good oxidizing agent with a potential for the III–II half-reaction of $+0.77$ volts. This means that iron (II) is stable with respect to oxidation by water but is unstable with respect to oxidation by oxygen of the air. No other oxidation states of iron are important in water. Osmium and ruthenium in their higher oxidation states are good oxidizing agents with potentials of a little less than $+1$. Most of the species present in these solutions are complex ions rather than the simple hydrated ions.

Cobalt (III) is such a good oxidizing agent that the free ion oxidizes water. But in the form of the complex ammine ion, this state is stable in water. This illustrates how complexing may affect the stability of a given oxidation state. Nickel has only the oxidation state (II) in water, the higher oxidation states being unstable with respect to reduction by water. The stable oxidation state for copper in water solution is (II). Copper (I) salts can be prepared in water solution, but only as insoluble compounds or in the form of complex ions such as $Cu(CN)_3{}^{2-}$. The free Cu^+ ion would disproportionate in aqueous solution. The silver (II) ion is a strong oxidizing agent and will oxidize water. Gold (III) is also a strong oxidizing agent, although complex ion formation makes the potential less positive.

Among the $4f$ inner-transitional elements, the only element which has an oxidation state greater than three in aqueous solution is cerium. The cerium (IV) is a good enough oxidizing agent to oxidize water, but the rate of reaction is so slow that for all practical purposes it doesn't go. Of the reduced states, only Eu(II) has a chance for more than a fleeting existence in water. It may be prepared by reduction with zinc and recovered from solution as the insoluble sulfate or carbonate. Samarium and ytterbium can only be reduced electrolytically or with sodium amalgam. The Sm^{2+} and Yb^{2+} ions are easily oxidized by water and oxygen of the air.

The ions of the $5f$ elements, however, show a larger number of oxidation states in water. Note how the oxidation state (III) increases in stability along the period. Uranium (III) is strong enough to reduce water, neptunium (III) is easily oxidized to the (IV) state by oxygen of the air, and plutonium (III) requires a reasonably strong oxidizing agent to take it to the (IV) state. Americium (IV) and curium (IV) are strong oxidizing agents in their own right and are easily reduced to the (III) state. The oxygenated cations of the (V) state show a similar increase in oxidizing power. The potentials for the VI–V half-reactions show an alternation of values which in combination with those of the V–IV half-reaction make the oxidation state (V) for uranium and plutonium unstable with respect to disproportionation:

$$4H^+ + 2UO_2{}^+ \rightarrow UO_2{}^{2+} + U^{4+} + 2H_2O$$

The (VI) state-oxygenated cations are good oxidizing agents.

V

Coordination Chemistry

A$_{\text{N}}$ aqueous solution made from solid violet $CrCl_3 \cdot 6H_2O$ changes from violet to green over a period of days at room temperature. This violet solid consists of $Cr(H_2O)_6^{3+}$ ions and chloride ions, which in solution slowly establish the equilibria described by the following net equations:

$$Cr(H_2O)_6^{3+} + Cl^- \rightleftarrows CrCl(H_2O)_5^{2+} + H_2O$$
$$\text{violet} \qquad\qquad \text{green}$$
$$CrCl(H_2O)_5^{2+} + Cl^- \rightleftarrows CrCl_2(H_2O)_4^+ + H_2O$$
$$\text{green}$$

These species are not in rapid equilibrium with their environment and are said to be inert; species which are in rapid equilibrium are said to be labile. The iron chloro species are examples of labile species, that is, $FeCl(H_2O)_5^{2+}$, $FeCl_2(H_2O)_4^+$, $FeCl_3(H_2O)_3$, and $FeCl_4^-$.

The existence of inert species leads to the very interesting situation that the individual components of such solutions may be isolated. Thus, from a solution containing $Cr(III)$ and Cl^-, three individual compounds each containing one of the species $Cr(H_2O)_6^{3+}$, $CrCl(H_2O)_5^{2+}$, and $CrCl_2(H_2O)_4^+$ may be isolated. Each compound when redissolved in water initially yields a solution containing only the components of the solid, only slowly establishing the equilibria described in the net equations. In contrast, a labile species such as $FeCl_3$ when dissolved in water instantaneously forms all possible species in concentrations determined by the magnitude of the equilibrium constants.

If chloride is the only anion present, then the compounds obtained from the solutions all have the same formula, namely, $CrCl_3 \cdot 6H_2O$. However, upon closer examination it will be found that the moles of chloride per mole of chromium in each compound as determined by silver ion precipitation will be 3, 2, and 1, instead of 3 for each compound. This suggests that the compounds are more properly formulated as $[Cr(H_2O)_6]Cl_3$, $[CrCl(H_2O)_5]Cl_2 \cdot H_2O$, and $[CrCl_2(H_2O)_4]Cl \cdot 2H_2O$ to distinguish the chloride which simply serves as an anion from the chloride ligands which are bonded to the central metal ion.

Compounds with the same composition but different properties are called isomers. Isomerism is one of the interesting facets of coordination compounds to be discussed in the following sections. Also to be discussed are those compounds containing a carbon-metal bond. These carbon-metal bonded compounds are of particular interest as intermediates in organic syntheses.

5–1   BONDING IN COORDINATION COMPOUNDS

Effect of Size

The number of ligands bonded to a central metal ion is determined by a variety of factors, among them the size of the central metal ion. The ion must be large enough to accommodate the ligands about it at distances which are reasonable for bonding. For a given coordination number there is an optimum ratio, radius central ion : radius ligand ion, below which the ligands cannot be accommodated. This is calculated in the manner described in Section 3–1. From these data it is concluded that normally the atoms of the second period, lithium to fluorine, are large enough to accommodate only four ligands in tetrahedral symmetry. All the elements beyond the second period are large enough to show coordination number six, although higher coordination numbers are possible for the later periods. Coordination number eight is possible for the atoms of the elements of the $4f$, $5f$, $3d$, $4d$, $5d$, and $6d$ periods. This is supported by the chemical facts.

Valence Bond Theory

In the valence bond theory, the ligand electrons are accommodated in the hybrid orbitals evolved from the metal orbitals of the central metal. These are d^2sp^3 orbitals in the octahedral case, dsp^2 in the square planar, and sp^3 for the tetrahedral case. Coordination number eight orbitals are d^5sp^2 or d^4sp^3; thus, only ions of the elements at the beginning of each series with d^0, d^1, or d^2 configurations are capable of forming such species, because the later members of the period do not have sufficient number of vacant d orbitals. Similarly, the low oxidation state ions of the last members of each period with d^7 and d^8 configurations have only one vacant d orbital and therefore are expected to form square planar complexes. Although the complexes for these species are largely square planar as expected, octahedral and tetrahedral species are also known. With the d^9 configuration, the d orbitals are filled, and the tetrahedral configuration of sp^3 would be expected. However, square-planar species such as $Cu(NH_3)_4^{2+}$ are known, the explanation of which requires the promotion of a d electron to a higher energy level. These restrictive properties, the accompanying difficulty in explaining some magnetic properties, and the inability to explain spectral properties have found the valence bond theory as applied to coordination chemistry in a position of diminishing usefulness.

Crystal (Ligand) Field Theory

The crystal field theory deals with the electrostatic interactions of the ligand ions with the central ion and the consequent effect of the field on the energy of the metal d orbitals. In Section 1–4, the effect of an octahedral field on the energy of the five d orbitals was shown to be the splitting of the orbitals into two energy groups, one triplet of lower energy than the unresolved d orbitals, and a doublet of higher energy than the unresolved d

orbitals. The energy separation between the two levels was designated as Δ. The theory has now been extended to include neutral polar ligands which are covalently bonded to the central metal ion and consequently is now called ligand field theory.

An important feature of the ligand field theory is the crystal field stabilization energy (cfse). The crystal field stabilization energy is the energy difference between a system in which the electrons are distributed preferentially in the triplet and doublet levels and a hypothetical system in which the same number of electrons occupy d orbitals all of which are at the same energy. An estimate of the relative crystal field stabilization energy can be made for coordination-number-six species on the assumption that its value for a d^{10} configuration is zero and with the knowledge that three pairs of electrons occupy the lower level triplet, and two pairs of electrons occupy the higher level doublet. Therefore, the contribution of each electron to the lower level must be $-2/5\Delta$, and the contribution of each electron to the higher level must be $+3/5\Delta$, since $6(-2/5\Delta) + 4(3/5\Delta) = 0$. The results of the calculation are given in Table 5–1. Note how the nature of the ligand influences the crystal field stabilization energy for the d^4 to d^7 configurations. Compare the values with the electron distributions shown in Figure 1–9. The magnetic properties of the complex will reflect the difference in the pairing of the electrons, and the

Table 5–1
Crystal Field Stabilization Energies (Units Δ) for Six-Coordinate Species

Electron Config.	Field Weak	Strong	Electron Config.	Field Weak	Strong
d^0, d^{10}	0	0	d^5	0	$\frac{10}{5}$
d^1	$\frac{2}{5}$	$\frac{2}{5}$	d^6	$\frac{2}{5}$	$\frac{12}{5}$
d^2	$\frac{4}{5}$	$\frac{4}{5}$	d^7	$\frac{4}{5}$	$\frac{9}{5}$
d^3	$\frac{6}{5}$	$\frac{6}{5}$	d^8	$\frac{6}{5}$	$\frac{6}{5}$
d^4	$\frac{3}{5}$	$\frac{8}{5}$	d^9	$\frac{3}{5}$	$\frac{3}{5}$

terms spin-free and spin-paired are used to distinguish the two arrangements of the same number of electrons.

Crystal field stabilization energy calculations may be made for each of the geometrical forms and then compared with one another for the purpose of predicting which geometry would be the most likely under the given conditions. Configurations with high crystal field stabilization energy will be favored over those with lower values. This comparison ignores some nonequivalent factors, but some useful generalizations can be made.

1. The magnitude of Δ depends upon the nature of the ligand, increasing in the order $I^- < Br^- < Cl^- < OH^- < F^- < H_2O < SCN^- < NH_3 < NO_2^- < CN^-$.

2. The elements of the $4d$ and $5d$ periods have a Δ which is 30% larger than the Δ of the $3d$ elements.

3. The magnitude of Δ for tetrahedral species is only 4/9 that of the Δ for the octahedral configuration.

4. Ions with d^0, d^5, and d^{10} configurations in which the crystal field stabilization energy is zero are likely to take tetrahedral geometry, because the ligand repulsion will be lower in this case than for octahedral or square-planar arrangements.

5. Square-planar complexes will be formed most likely with strong field ligands and with ion configurations d^8 and d^9.

6. Octahedral configurations will be favored for the ions with d^3 and d^6 configurations with either weak field or strong field ligands. Ions of other configurations also have octahedral geometry but are likely also to have species which are tetrahedral or distorted octahedral.

7. Coordination-number-six species, except for those with d^3, spin-paired d^6, or zero crystal field stabilization energy, are likely to have a geometry distorted from the octahedral geometry. This may occur by elongation of the distances perpendicular to the plane of the four ligands and a shortening of the distance within this plane. The resulting geometry is tetragonal, and it is intermediate between the octahedral and square-planar configurations. This occurs since partially filled orbitals of the same energy gain a

measure of stability by going to separate energy levels. This is called the Jahn-Teller effect.

Molecular Orbital Theory

In the crystal field theory, the donation of the ligand electron pairs to the central metal ion, that is, the covalent character of the bond, is not really considered because the calculations are based on an electrostatic model. Although this has been modified in the

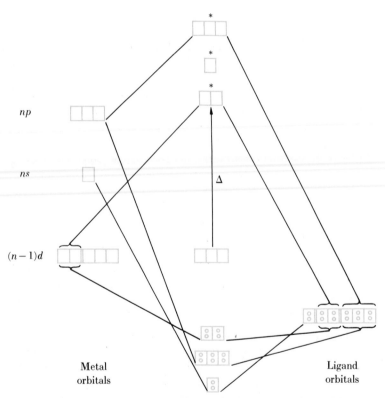

Figure 5–1 Molecular orbitals of a complex Ma₆ with octahedral symmetry. Single bonds only.

ligand theory, the whole problem of orbitals for both the metal electrons and ligand electrons can be described more effectively in the molecular orbital theory of chemical bonding. A qualitative description of the theory as applied to coordination-number-six species for single-bonded ligands follows.

In this, the nine atomic orbitals of the metal, that is, five *d*, one *s*, and three *p*, are combined with the six orbitals of the electron pairs of the ligand to give fifteen new orbitals which are common to all the nuclei. These orbitals combine and are ordered with respect to energy content according to the diagram of Figure 5–1. The ligand electron pairs and the metal electrons are then distributed in the orbitals in order of increasing energy content. Thus, the six bonding electron pairs occupy the lowest six orbitals, which for coordination number six, approximates the hybridized orbitals of Pauling d^2sp^3. These orbitals are called bonding orbitals. In the generation of these orbitals, an equivalent number of high energy orbitals are formed. These are called antibonding orbitals and are designated with an asterisk. Note that the three remaining orbitals remain essentially metallic orbitals. These are designated as nonbonding orbitals. The energy separation between the nonbonding and the lowest of the antibonding orbitals is the ligand field separation. The introduction of electrons into the antibonding orbitals has the effect of weakening the bonding orbitals. To avoid rewriting this diagram each time, a more compact arrangement introduced by J. W. Linnett, the English theoretical chemist, will be used (Figure 5–2). Similar diagrams have been created for the square planar and tetrahedral configurations.

5–2   REACTION RATES AND ELECTRON CONFIGURATIONS

Coordination Number Six

Professor Henry Taube, of Stanford University, was the first to correlate the experimental inertness or lability of an ion or molecule and the electron distribution in the complex as described by the valence bond theory. The 6-coordinate ions of the transitional elements as described by the valence bond theory fall into two categories: those in which the ligand electron pairs are accommo-

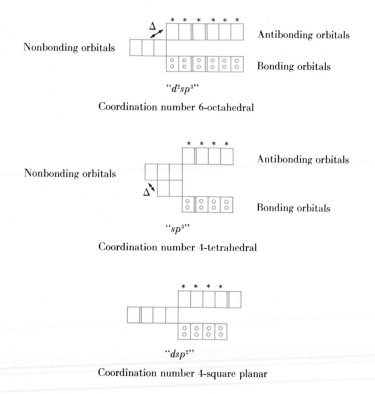

Figure 5–2   Abridged molecular orbital diagrams.

dated in hybridized orbitals using inner d orbitals of the central metal, that is, $(n - 1)d^2nsnp^3$, and those using outer d orbitals, $nsnp^3nd^2$. The separation of species between inert and labile is sharpest in the inner orbital class, where those inner orbital species with a vacant d orbital are labile and those with all the d orbitals occupied are inert. Table 5–2 contains examples of inert and labile inner-orbital complexes. Transitional elements with d^4 to d^6 electrons exhibit inert inner-orbital complexes with strong field ligands, but labile complexes of the outer-orbital type with weak field ligands. For example, $Fe(CN)_6^{3-}$, an outer-orbital complex, is

Table 5–2
Complex Ions with Inner Orbitals Occupied by Ligand Electrons

		Inner orbitals	$(n-1)d^2nsnp^3$ hybridized orbitals	
d^0	$Sc(L)^{3+}$	— — —	○○ ○○ ○○	labile
d^1	$Ti(L)_6^{3+}$	↓ — —	○○ ○○ ○○	labile
d^2	$V(L)_6^{3+}$	↓ ↓ —	○○ ○○ ○○	labile
d^3	$Cr(L)_6^{3+}$	↓ ↓ ↓	○○ ○○ ○○	inert
to d^6	$Co(L)_6^{3+}$	↕ ↕ ↕	○○ ○○ ○○	inert
	L = ligand		$(n-1)d^2nsnp^3$ hybridized orbitals	

inert, and FeF_6^{3-}, an outer-orbital complex, is labile. With the weak field ligands, the d^5 electrons occupy two of the antibonding orbitals, thus weakening the metal ligand bond (Fig. 5–3).

Outer-orbital complexes are not necessarily all labile. They become more inert as the formal charge on the central atom and the degree of covalency increase. An example from the p electron elements illustrates this particularly well. The sequence AlF_6^{3-}, SiF_6^{2-}, PF_6^-, SF_6 covers the range from labile to inert as the oxidation state of the central atom increases from III to VI.

Actually, the basis for classifying ions as inert or labile is the reaction rate, which in turn is related to the energy required for the

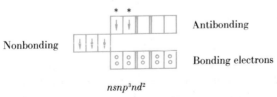

$nsnp^3nd^2$

Figure 5–3 Distribution of electrons in the FeF_6^{3-} ion.

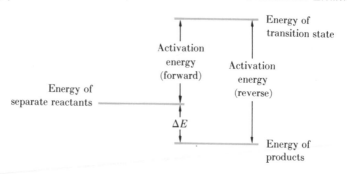

Figure 5–4   Activation energy.

formation of the complex unit of reactants in which the bonds are broken and reformed into new species. This energy is called the activation energy, and the complex unit of reactants is called the transition state (Figure 5–4). A slow reaction has a high activation energy, and a fast reaction has a low activation energy. Now, on the basis of the crystal field stabilization energy alone, it can be seen from the data of Table 5–1 that for the configurations d^4 to d^7, all other factors being equal, the strong field complexes (comparable to inner complexes in the Taube scheme) would be expected to be more inert than the weak field (outer-orbital) complexes. The other configurations have the same crystal field stabilization energy, and other factors must be invoked to determine their relative inertness and lability.

All other factors are not necessarily equal. There are two possible transition states to be considered. In one, the six-coordinated species accepts the ligand to be substituted, thereby forming a seven-coordinate intermediate, which eliminates a ligand and returns to a six-coordinated species of different composition. This is referred to as an S_{N2} mechanism, which stands for substitution, nucleophilic, bimolecular. However, there is an alternate route through a five-coordinate, square-pyramidal transition state, formed by an initial dissociation process and followed by the addition of the substituting ligand to reform a six-coordinate species (Figure 5–5). This is generally referred to as an S_{N1} mechanism,

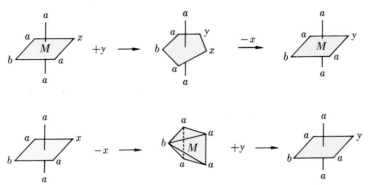

Figure 5–5 Possible routes for substitution of ligands in coordination number six.

which means substitution, nucleophilic, monomolecular. A rational for inertness or lability must recognize either route.

Professors Basolo and Pearson of Northwestern University, have calculated the net loss in crystal field stabilization energy which occurs when the six-coordinated species transforms into either the five- or seven-coordinate species. It is assumed that if the crystal field stabilization energy for the transition state is higher than that for the six-coordinate species, then the activation energy for the process will be lower and the species will be labile. If the reverse is true, then the activation energy will be high and the species will be inert. The result of such calculations (Table 5–3) for the strong-field case is that the d^3, d^4, d^5, d^6, and d^8 species should be inert compared to the others, and that the degree of inertness varies $d^8 \sim d^5 < d^4 < d^3 < d^6$. In a weak field, only d^3 and d^8 should be inert. These data fit the chemical facts reasonably well, although the d^8 configuration as represented by $Ni(H_2O)_6^{2+}$ is not normally considered inert compared to the d^3 species $Cr(H_2O)_6^{3+}$. On the other hand, the difference in charge is significant, and a comparison should only be made between ions of the same charge.

The seven-coordinated transition state utilizes the vacant d orbital of the central metal in the case of the labile species. On the other hand an ion with filled d orbitals requires the promotion of

Table 5–3

Change in Crystal Field Stabilization Energy (Units Δ) Upon Transforming a Six-Coordinate Species to a Five- or Seven-Coordinated Species

Number of Electrons	Strong Field CN 5	CN 7	Weak Field CN 5	CN 7
0	0	0	0	0
1	−0.06	−0.13	−0.06	−0.13
2	−0.11	−0.26	−0.11	−0.26
3	0.20	0.42	0.20	0.43
4	0.14	0.30	−0.31	0.11
5	0.09	0.17	0	0
6	0.40	0.85	−0.06	−0.13
7	−0.11	0.53	−0.11	−0.26
8	0.20	0.43	0.20	0.43
9	−0.31	0.11	−0.31	0.11
10	0	0	0	0

an electron to vacate a d orbital or involves a higher energy orbital in the formation of the transition state, thus requiring a high activation energy which results in a slow rate of reaction. The S_{N1} dissociation process to a five-coordinate transition state is favored in species in which some of the antibonding orbitals are occupied.

Coordination Number Four

All tetrahedral species are labile. The square-planar species of the $5d$ element platinum are very inert. This simply means that the activation energy for the substitution process is high. Like the six-coordinate species, the four-coordinate species have alternate routes by which substitution may occur. Actually, two solvent molecules probably occupy positions perpendicular to the plane bearing the four ligands, and thus the mechanism of reaction in fact involves a six-coordinate species with a distorted octahedral

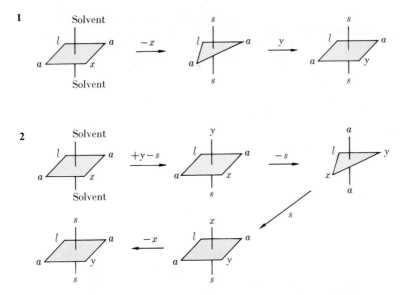

Figure 5–6 Possible routes for substitution of ligands in four-coordinate square planar species.

symmetry (Figure 5–6). There is some evidence that substitution involving ligands with weak trans directing properties (Section 5–3) go via path 1, and those involving strong trans directing ligands go via path 2. Palladium complexes in general are more labile than platinum, but more inert than nickel.

5–3   CHEMISTRY OF COORDINATION NUMBER FOUR

In the previous discussion, it was pointed out that ions with d^8 and d^9 configurations particularly favor the square planar arrangement. This is amply supported by the vast amount of chemical data on compounds of nickel (II), platinum (II), and palladium (II), only a small portion of which shall be reported here. The more inert character of palladium and platinum, as compared to compounds of nickel with the same ligand, reflects the greater crys-

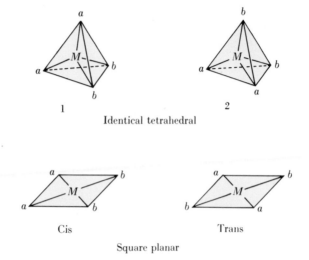

Figure 5–7   **Configurations for complexes of the composition Ma_2b_2.**

tal field stabilization energy of the $4d$ and $5d$ elements.   Before
reading this section, it would be well for the reader to review the
rules of coordination compound nomenclature outlined in the Appendix.

Platinum

Many years before the modern era of atomic structure, Alfred
Werner, a great name in coordination chemistry, correctly answered the question of the configuration of the four-coordinate
complexes of platinum which confronted the investigators of that
time.   Two different compounds with the composition $Pt(NH_3)_2Cl_2$
had been prepared.   Both were neutral molecules, but they differed
slightly in color and solubility.   One, α, was prepared by the reaction of ammonia with the tetrachloroplatinate (II) ion:

$$PtCl_4^{2-} + 2NH_3 \rightarrow Pt(NH_3)_2Cl_2\ (\alpha) + 2Cl^-$$

The second, β, was prepared by the action of chloride ion with the tetrammine platinum (II) cation:

$$Pt(NH_3)_4^{2+} + 2Cl^- \rightarrow Pt(NH_3)_2Cl_2 \ (\beta) + 2NH_3$$

Assuming that the compounds are neutral and monomeric, and that the most likely geometry is either tetrahedral or square planar, then the mere existence of the two compounds with the same composition requires the square-planar arrangement, because the tetrahedral molecule Ma_2b_2 does not exist as isomers. Rotation (Figure 5–7) of tetrahedron 1 gives tetrahedron 2, but there is no manipulation which converts square plane 1 to square plane 2. The isomer with like groups adjacent to one another is called the *cis* isomer, and the one with like groups opposed to one another is called the *trans* isomer.

The sequence of reactions probably occurring in the formation of the original cis and trans dichlorodiammine platinum (II) can be written in structural form, as shown in Equations 5–1 and 5–2.

$$\begin{bmatrix} Cl & & Cl \\ & Pt & \\ Cl & & Cl \end{bmatrix}^{2-} + NH_3 \longrightarrow \begin{bmatrix} H_3N & & Cl \\ & Pt & \\ Cl & & Cl \end{bmatrix}^{1-} + NH_3 \longrightarrow$$

$$\begin{bmatrix} H_3N & & NH_3 \\ & Pt & \\ Cl & & Cl \end{bmatrix} \qquad (5\text{–}1)$$

orange-yellow cis

$$\begin{bmatrix} H_3N & & NH_3 \\ & Pt & \\ H_3N & & NH_3 \end{bmatrix}^{2+} \cdot + Cl^- \longrightarrow \begin{bmatrix} H_3N & & NH_3 \\ & Pt & \\ H_3N & & Cl \end{bmatrix}^{1+} + Cl^- \longrightarrow$$

$$\begin{bmatrix} Cl & & NH_3 \\ & Pt & \\ H_3N & & Cl \end{bmatrix} \qquad (5\text{–}2)$$

sulfur-yellow-trans

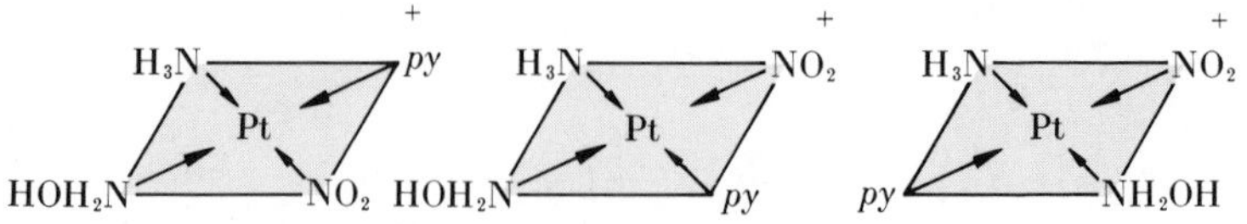

$$
\begin{array}{ccc}
\overset{+}{\text{H}_3\text{N}} \diagup py & \overset{+}{\text{H}_3\text{N}} \diagup \text{NO}_2 & \overset{+}{\text{H}_3\text{N}} \diagup \text{NO}_2 \\
\text{Pt} & \text{Pt} & \text{Pt} \\
\text{HOH}_2\text{N} - \text{NO}_2 & \text{HOH}_2\text{N} \diagdown py & py \diagdown \text{NH}_2\text{OH}
\end{array}
$$

Figure 5–8   Configuration for the isomers of
$[\text{Pt}(\text{NH}_3)(\text{py})(\text{NH}_2\text{OH})(\text{NO}_2)]^+$.

Note that in these reactions the substitution takes place preferentially at the position trans to the most electronegative ligand. This is one example of the phenomenon referred to as the trans effect. There has been established a list of ligands in order of increasing trans directing power as follows:

$$
\text{H}_2\text{O} < \text{OH}^- < \text{NH}_3 < \text{pyridine} < \text{Cl}^- < \text{Br}^- < \text{SCN}^- \sim \text{I}^-
$$
$$
\sim \text{NO}_2^- \sim \text{SO}_3\text{H}^- \sim \text{PR}_3 < \text{NO} < \text{CO} \sim \text{C}_2\text{H}_4 \sim \text{CN}^-
$$

The explanation of this phenomenon is not simple and involves more than electronegativity. Those ligands with strongest trans-directing properties possess orbitals which may accept electrons from the metal ion thus establishing multiple bond character in the metal ligand bond. The Russian chemist Tscherniaev used this principle in developing the synthesis for the three isomers of composition $\text{Pt}(\text{NH}_3)(\text{NO}_2)(\text{py})(\text{NH}_2\text{OH})^+$ (Figure 5–8). This, by the way, also is evidence for the square-planar configuration of the platinum complexes, since the tetrahedral geometry would not yield geometrical isomers.

In agreement with the assignment of the cis arrangement to the α form of $\text{Pt}(\text{NH}_3)_2\text{Cl}_2$, it reacts with a ligand molecule containing two donor atoms to displace two cis ligands. This molecule, called a bidentate ligand, is capable of spanning cis positions but not trans positions. No reaction is observed with the trans $\text{Pt}(\text{NH}_3)_2\text{Cl}_2$. The bidentate ligand in this case is ethylenediamine, $\text{NH}_2\text{CH}_2\text{CH}_2\text{NH}_2$. The reaction is written as in Equation 5–3.

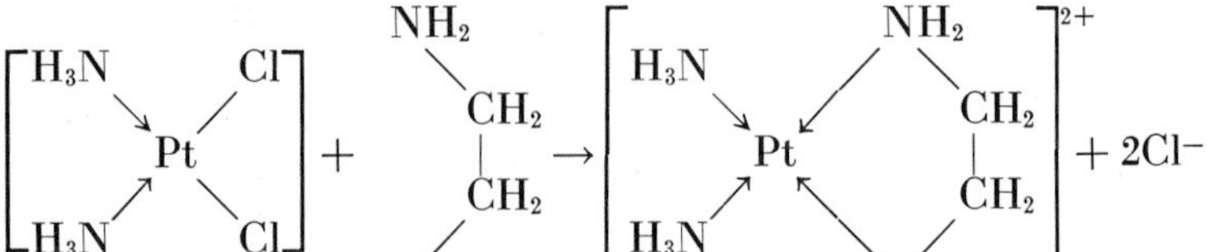

$$
\begin{bmatrix} \text{H}_3\text{N} & \text{Cl} \\ & \text{Pt} & \\ \text{H}_3\text{N} & \text{Cl} \end{bmatrix} +
\begin{matrix} \text{NH}_2 \\ \text{CH}_2 \\ | \\ \text{CH}_2 \\ \text{NH}_2 \end{matrix}
\rightarrow
\begin{bmatrix} \text{H}_3\text{N} & \text{NH}_2 \\ & \text{Pt} & \begin{matrix}\text{CH}_2 \\ | \\ \text{CH}_2\end{matrix} \\ \text{H}_3\text{N} & \text{NH}_2 \end{bmatrix}^{2+} + 2\text{Cl}^-
$$

$$(5\text{–}3)$$

Palladium

As expected the chemistry of palladium in the oxidation state (II) is similar to that of platinum. Geometrical isomers of $Pd(NH_3)_2Cl_2$, $Pd(py)_2Cl_2$, and $Pd(NH_3)_2(NO_2)_2$ are known, although palladium favors the formation of the trans isomers and in some instances is the only isomer known. Palladium compounds are more likely to undergo intramolecular re-arrangement during a reaction, as evidenced by the fact that trans $Pd(NH_3)_2Cl_2$ reacts with oxalate ion, $C_2O_4^{2-}$ to give $Pd(C_2O_4)(NH_3)_2$ which must be a cis compound (Equation 5–4).

$$\begin{bmatrix} Cl & NH_3 \\ & Pd & \\ H_3N & Cl \end{bmatrix} + \begin{matrix} O^- \\ C \\ C \\ O_- \end{matrix} \rightarrow \begin{bmatrix} H_3N & O \\ & Pd & C \\ H_3N & O \end{bmatrix} + 2Cl^-$$

$$(5\text{–}4)$$

Nickel

Nickel in the oxidation state (II) also has a d^8 configuration and with unidentate ligands usually forms labile square-planar complexes. The ions $Ni(CN)_4^{2-}$ and $Ni(NH_3)_4^{2+}$ are examples. Because of their lability, no geometrical isomers are known for nickel with unidentate ligands. Even though bidentate ligands usually result in complexes which are more inert, cis-trans isomerism has been observed only in a few cases. One example is that of the substituted gyloxime shown in Figure 5–9.

A growing number of tetrahedral nickel (II) species are being reported. The $NiCl_4^{2-}$ ion has been identified as a tetrahedral species in a fused salt system, and the compounds $(\phi_3AsO)_2NiCl_2$ and $[Et_4N]^+ [\phi_3PNiBr_3]^-$ are known to have nickel in tetrahedral symmetry.

Magnetic Properties. The square-planar complexes are diamagnetic and thus have the spin-paired configuration (Figure 5–10). The tetrahedral complexes in principle can be either spin-free or spin-paired, although the known compounds in the solid state are spin-free. This is presently a subject of interest to research workers.

$$H_3C-C\text{———}C-CH_2C_6H_5$$

Cis

$$H_5C_6H_2C-C\text{———}C-CH_3$$

Trans

Figure 5–9 Cis-trans isomers of bis (benzylmethylglyoximates) nickel (II).

5–4 CHEMISTRY OF COORDINATION NUMBER SIX

The metal ions with d^3 and d^6 electron configurations were shown to be inert (Section 5–1). This is supported by extensive chemistry of the Cr(III) and Co(III) complex compounds. Although all the other elements also show coordination number six,

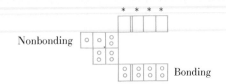

Spin-free tetrahedral

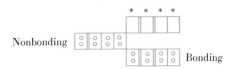

Spin-paired square planar

Figure 5–10 Electron distributions for complex ions derived from metal ions with a d^8 configuration square planar Pt(II), Pd(II), Ni(II), tetrahedral Ni(II).

the chemistry of chromium and cobalt will be dealt with here almost exclusively.

Geometrical Isomerism

   Unidentate Ligands. The structures of species with octahedral geometry will be drawn as shown in Figure 5–11. The reader

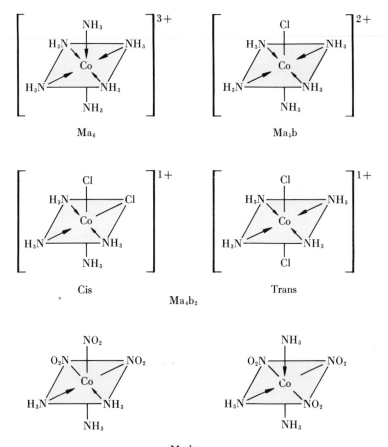

Figure 5–11 Geometrical isomerism with unidentate ligands in coordination number six.

must remember that all six points are drawn equidistant from the center and opposing positions are always trans. The general class of compounds Ma_6, with six identical unidentate ligands, is illustrated by the following: aquo species $Cr(H_2O)_6^{3+}$; ammine species, $Co(NH_3)_6^{3+}$, $Cr(NH_3)_6^{3+}$; and the anionic species, $Co(NO_2)_6^{3-}$; and $Cr(CN)_6^{3-}$.

All the ligand positions of the Ma_6 species are equivalent, and therefore in monosubstituted species of the class Ma_5b, no isomers are possible. The location of the substituent in the drawing is of no consequence. Compounds of many unidentate ligands have been prepared, including all the halogens, NO_2^-, NO_3^-, SO_4^{2-}, CN^-, SCN^-, OH^-, and organic sulfides, amines, phosphines, arsines, and stibines. Examples are $CrCl(H_2O)_5^{2+}$, $CrCl(NH_3)_5^{2+}$, and $CoCl(NH_3)_5^{2+}$.

The substitution can be carried another step to produce compounds of the general composition Ma_4b_2. In this case, the five sites of the monosubstituted derivative are not all equivalent, and the second b ligand can go into two different locations, either cis or trans to the first substituent (Figure 5–11). Cis and trans isomers of these compounds have different colors. For instance, in the cobalt ammine series, the trans dichlorotetrammine cobalt (III) is green, and the cis compound is purple. A large number of cis-trans isomers are known, a small sample of which are given here: $[Co(NH_3)_4(H_2O)_2]^{3+}$, $[Pt(py)_2Cl_4]$, $[Ru(NH_3)_4Br_2]^+$, $[Ir(py)_2Cl_4]^-$, $[Co(NO_2)_4(NH_3)_2]^-$, and $[Cr(NH_3)_2(SCN)_4]^-$.

There is also the class of six-coordinate compounds in which three ligands of two different kinds are present, Ma_3b_3. Examples of this are $Co(NH_3)_3(NO_2)_3$, and $Cr(SCN)_3(NH_3)_3$. There are two different ways in which these ligands may be arranged, either three of one kind on a face of the octahedron (cis), or three along an edge of the octahedron (trans) as shown in Figure 5–11.

Many other types of compounds can be formed by increasing the number of different kinds of unidentate groups. In fact, a compound of platinum (IV) has been prepared in which six different ligands are bonded to the platinum, Ptabcdef. There are fifteen different ways in which these six ligands can be arranged, and each exists as optical isomers.

Optical Isomers

Introduction of Bidentate Ligands. A bidentate ligand occupies two positions. Therefore, the simplest composition for six-coordinate compounds with one bidentate group is $M(AA)a_4$. Ethylenediamine, oxalate anion, and carbonate ion are three of the most common symmetrical bidentate ligands. The carbonatotetrammine cobalt (III) cation is an important starting material for substitution reactions in which cis isomers are prepared, because the carbonato group can span only a cis position. Carbon dioxide is eliminated by hydrogen ion attack of the carbonato group, followed by insertion of the substituting ligands. This works only if the reaction conditions are such that no ligand rearrangement takes place.

Two bidentate ligands replace four unidentate ligands to give a species of composition $M(AA)_2a_2$. Here, there are two ways in which the bidentate groups may be arranged, either with the unidentate ligand cis or the unidentate ligands trans (Figure 5–12). It is important to note that the mirror image of the cis isomer is nonsuperimposable on the original, while the mirror image of the trans form is superimposable on the original. In a synthesis, the two cis forms are obtained in equal amounts because the properties of these isomers (enantiomorphs) are the same except that one rotates plane-polarized light to the left (levo), and the other rotates it an equal number of degrees to the right (dextro). The optical isomers can be separated by the addition of an optically active anion if the unresolved species is present as a cation, or an optically active cation if the unresolved species is an anion. Thus, if *d*-tartrate (an anion) is added to a solution containing *d* and *l* $Co(en)_2Cl_2^+$, a precipitate is formed which contains the one form of the cation and the *d* tartrate anion, and the other form of the cation remains in solution. Such pairs of ions themselves are isomers and are called diasterioisomers. They often differ radically in solubility, and it is on this basis that a separation of optical isomers can be made. The wave length of the polarized light used must be identified since the magnitude and sign of rotation are a function of the wave length used.

$$\left[\begin{array}{c} H_2 \\ H_2N-C \diagdown_{CH_2} \\ H_3N \quad NH_2 \\ Co \\ H_3N \quad NH_3 \\ NH_3 \end{array} \right]^{3+} \qquad \left[\begin{array}{c} O \\ O-C \diagdown_{O} \\ H_3N \\ Co \\ H_3N \quad NH_3 \\ NH_3 \end{array} \right]^{1+}$$

Class M(*AA*)a₄

$$\left[\begin{array}{c} Cl \\ H_2 \quad H_2 \\ H_2C-N \quad N \\ H_2C \quad Co \quad CH_2 \\ N \quad N \quad CH_2 \\ H_2 \quad H_2 \\ Cl \end{array} \right]^{+}$$

Trans

$$\begin{array}{cc} H_2 \quad +1 \\ H_2N-C \diagdown_{CH_2} \\ Cl \quad NH_2 \\ Co \\ Cl \quad NH_2 \\ H_2N \diagdown_{CH_2} \\ C \\ H_2 \end{array} \qquad \begin{array}{c} H_2 \quad +1 \\ C \diagdown_{NH_2} \\ H_2C \\ H_2N \quad Cl \\ Co \\ H_2N \quad Cl \\ H_2C \diagdown_{C-NH_2} \\ H_2 \end{array}$$

Class M(*AA*)₂a₂   Cis

Mirror images

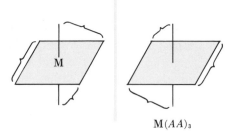

M(*AA*)₃

Figure 5–12 Isomers containing bidentate groups. The bidentate group is represented by ⌒.

The substitution by bidentate ligands can be carried one step further to give compounds of the general class $M(AA)_3$. These compounds may be either cations, $Cr(en)_3{}^{3+}$, $Co(en)_3{}^{3+}$, neutral molecules $Cr(acac)_3$, $Co(acac)_3$, or anions $Cr(C_2O_4)_3{}^{3-}$ and $Co(C_2O_4)_3{}^{3-}$. As shown in Figure 5–12, these compounds do not have superimposable mirror images, and therefore exist as optical isomers. These compounds are resolved in the same way as described above except for the neutral species, which require a different technique. The neutral species are much more difficult to separate and preferential adsorption upon an optically active surface such as d-quartz is often used.

A wide variety of different compounds have been resolved, some of which are tabulated in Table 5–4. The variety may be increased by using unsymmetrical bidentate ligands such as glycine NH_2CH_2COOH, multidentate ligands with three-, four-, five-, and even six-coordinating centers, as well as mixed unidentate ligands to give classes such as $M(AA)_2bc$, and $M(AA)_2ab$.

When Werner originally prepared and resolved optical isomers, the idea of optically active inorganic compounds was not easily accepted. There remained the idea that somehow the optical activity was related to the presence of the carbon atoms. To eliminate this possibility he prepared and resolved a compound in which the bidentate group was wholly inorganic, $Co(NH_3)_4(OH)_2{}^+$. In this ion the OH groups are the coordinating ligands, and because the central metal also is cobalt, the composition of the complex ion is $Co(Co(NH_3)_4(OH)_2)_3{}^{6+}$. The structural arrangement is given in Figure 5–13.

Table 5–4
Some Six-Coordinate Ions Which Have Been Resolved

$Cr(en)_3{}^{3+}$	$Co(en)_2(NH_3)_2{}^{3+}$	$Cr(C_2O_4)_3{}^{3-}$
$Co(en)_3{}^{3+}$	$Co(en)_2Cl_2{}^+$	$Co(C_2O_4)_3{}^{3-}$
$Ir(en)_3{}^{3+}$	$Ir(en)_2(NO_2)_2{}^+$	$Ni(dipy)_3{}^{2+}$
$Rh(en)_3{}^{3+}$	$Co(en)_2NH_3(NCS)^{2+}$	$Fe(dipy)_3{}^{3+}$
$Cr(en)_2C_2O_4{}^+$	$Ir(C_2O_4)_2Cl_2{}^{-3}$	$Os(dipy)_3{}^{3+}$

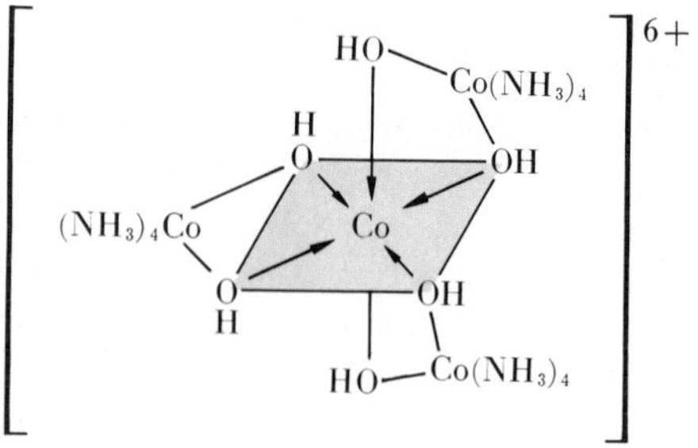

Figure 5–13   Werner's totally inorganic optically active ion [Co [Co(NH$_3$)$_4$(OH)$_2$]$_3$]$^{6+}$.

Table 5–5

Magnetic Moments of 3d Compounds (Coordination Number Six)

Number of d electrons	Compound	Spin-free Exptl.	Theory		Spin-paired Exptl.	Theory
d^1	VO(acac)$_2$	1.73	1.73	—	—	
	CrOCl$_5$	1.82				
d^2	V(NH$_3$)$_6$Cl$_3$	2.74	2.83	—	—	
	K$_3$CrF$_6$	2.80				
d^3	Cr(NH$_3$)$_6$I$_3$	3.71				
	Cr(en)$_3$I$_3$	3.92	3.86	—	—	
	K$_3$Cr(CN)$_6$	3.72				
d^4	Mn(acac)$_3$	4.95	4.90	K$_3$Mn(CN)$_6$	3.18	2.83
d^5	K$_2$Mn(C$_2$O$_4$)$_3$·2H$_2$O	5.86	5.92	K$_3$Fe(CN)$_6$	2.40	1.73
	(NH$_4$)$_3$FeF$_6$	5.98				
d^6	K$_3$CoF$_6$	4.26	4.90	Co(NH$_3$)$_6$$^{3+}$	0	0
				Co(en)$_3$$^{3+}$	0	0
d^7	Co(NH$_3$)$_6$$^{2+}$	5.40	3.86	Co(NO$_2$)$_4$$^{4-}$	1.85	1.73
d^8	Ni(en)$_3$$^{2+}$	3.16	2.83	—		
	Ni(NH$_3$)$_6$$^{2+}$	3.11				

Magnetic Properties

The six-coordinate species of the $3d$ transitional elements by and large show the magnetic properties expected for the spin-only relationship for either the spin-free or spin-paired configuration (Table 5–5). Values larger than theoretical may be encountered with ions of the elements in the last half of the period. The six-coordinate species of the $4d$ and $5d$ elements are more than likely spin-paired because of the larger Δ and very often have magnetic moments larger than expected for the spin-only relationship. The larger values are due to the fact that the orbital contribution is not completely quenched and therefore makes some contribution to the total magnetic moment.

Other Forms of Isomerism

In addition to geometrical and optical isomerism, there are a variety of ways in which the ligands may be arranged for the same composition. These may be classified as follows:

1. Coordination Isomerism. In this type of isomerism the ligands are distributed between an anion and cation to give the following extremes and all possible intermediates.

   $[Co(NH_3)_6]^{3+}[Cr(NO_2)_6]^{3-}$ and $[Cr(NH_3)_6]^{3+}[Co(NO_2)_6]^{3-}$

   $[Cu(NH_3)_4]^{2+}[PtCl_4]^{2-}$ and $[Pt(NH_3)_4]^{2+}[CuCl_4]^{2-}$

   $[Cr(NH_3)_6]^{3+}[Cr(SCN)_6]^{3-}$ and
   $$[Cr(NH_3)_4(SCN)_2]^{+}[Cr(NH_3)_2(SCN)_4]^{-}$$

2. Hydrate Isomerism. The chromium chloride complexes mentioned in the initial paragraphs of this chapter are examples of this class along with compounds such as

   $$[Co(NH_3)_4H_2OCl]^{2+}2Cl^{-} \text{ and } [Co(NH_3)_4(Cl)_2]^{+}Cl^{-}\cdot H_2O$$

3. Ionization Isomerism. These compounds yield different anions in solution, thus:

   $[Co(NH_3)_5NO_3]^{2+}SO_4^{2-}$ and $[Co(NH_3)_5SO_4]^{+}NO_3^{-}$

   $[Co(en)_2ClNO_2]^{+}NO_2^{-}$ and $[Co(en)_2NO_2]^{+}Cl^{-}$

4. Structural Isomerism. There are only a few examples of this case in which the bonding of a ligand is through different atoms. In the compounds

$$[Co(NH_3)_5ONO]^{2+}2Cl^- \text{ and } [Co(NH_3)_5NO_2]^{2+}2Cl^-$$

the O bonded ONO is unstable and reverts to the N bonded compound. Recently, Basolo has prepared the compounds

$$[(\phi_3As)_2Pd(NCS)_2] \text{ and } [(\phi_3As)_2(SCN)_2]$$

in which the thiocyanato group is bonded through the N in one case and the S in the other.

Coordination Number Eight

The elements, zirconium, hafnium, thorium, cerium, tungsten, molybdenum, rhenium, and uranium in the oxidation state four form compounds in which the central atom is surrounded by eight ligands with either the square antiprism or dodecahedron arrangement. Although the possibilities for isomerism exist, none have been found. Typical compounds are the neutral acetylacetone derivatives $Zr(acac)_4$, and anionic species such as $Hf(C_2O_4)_4^{4-}$ and $Mo(CN)_8^{4-}$. The oxalate anionic species are labile as are the substitution products of the octacyano anions.

5–5   METAL CARBONYLS

Compounds containing a metal and carbon monoxide are called carbonyls. The first such compound, nickel carbonyl $Ni(CO)_4$, was discovered in 1890. These compounds are of special interest now because of their importance as intermediates in organic synthesis. Our interest will be with the simple volatile carbonyls and some of their reactions.

Preparations

The simplest preparative method is the direct addition of carbon monoxide to the metal.

$$Ni_{(s)} + 4CO_{(g)} \rightarrow Ni(CO)_{4(g)}$$

This goes easily at room temperature with nickel, and at about 200° and 100 atmospheres pressure with iron. The other carbonyls are prepared more satisfactorily by other routes. Osmium, rhenium, and technetium carbonyls have been prepared by direct reaction of the oxide with carbon monoxide at 200 to 20 atmospheres and 150° to 200°.

$$Re_2O_7 + 17CO \rightarrow Re_2(CO)_{10} + 7CO_2$$

More frequently a metal halide and carbon monoxide react in the presence of a reducing agent such as a metal or a Grignard reagent such as C_6H_5MgBr.

$$RuI_3 + 3Ag + 5CO \xrightarrow[\text{450 atmospheres}]{170°} Ru(CO)_5 + 3AgI$$

The chromium, molybdenum, and tungsten carbonyls are usually prepared with the Grignard reagent. The latest addition to the carbonyl family is $V(CO)_6$. It is formed by the reaction described by the following equation:

$$2VCl_3 + 2Mg\text{-}Zn + 12CO \xrightarrow[\substack{\text{pyridine} \\ 135° \text{ and } 20 \text{ atmospheres}}]{I_2} 2V(CO)_6 + 2MgCl_2 + ZnCl_2$$

The compound is paramagnetic, in agreement with its monomeric nature. The anions $V(CO)_6^-$, $Nb(CO)_6^-$, and $Ta(CO)_6^-$ have been prepared by reduction with metallic sodium in a nonaqueous solvent.

Properties of the Carbonyls

The physical properties of the known carbonyls are listed in Table 5–6. In general these compounds are insoluble in water and soluble in organic solvents. They may be flammable and are toxic. They are thermally decomposed to the metal and carbon monoxide at relatively low temperatures, and in the presence of ultraviolet light, they tend to polymerize.

$$Fe(CO)_5 \xrightarrow{h\nu} Fe_2(CO)_9 \xrightarrow{h\nu} Fe_3(CO)_{12}$$

Table 5-6
Physical Properties of the Volatile Carbonyls

	$V(CO)_6$	$Cr(CO)_6$	$Mn_2(CO)_{10}$	$Fe(CO)_5$	$Co_2(CO)_8$	$Ni(CO)_4$
mp	d 70°	Sub. 20°	154° to 156°	−20°	51°	−25°
bp	—	—	—	103°	—	143°
		$Mo(CO)_6$	$Tc_2(CO)_{10}$	$Fe(CO)_9$		
mp		Sub. 50°	159° to 160°	d 100°		
bp		—	—			
		$W(CO)_6$	$Re_2(CO)_{10}$	$Fe_3(CO)_{12}$	$Co_3(CO)_{12}$	
mp		Sub.	Sub. 177°	d 140°	d 60°	
bp		—	d 400°	—	—	
				$Ru(CO)_5$	$Rh_2(CO)_8$	
mp				−22°	d 76°	
				$Ru_3(CO)_{12}$	$Rh_4(CO)_{12}$	
mp				—	—	
					$Rh_6(CO)_{16}$	
mp					—	
				$Os(CO)_5$	$Ir_2(CO)_8$	
mp				−15°	Subl.	
				$Os_3(CO)_{12}$	$Ir_4(CO)_{12}$	
mp				224°	d 210°	

The carbonyls undergo substitution reactions with other donor ligands, such as amines and substituted phosphines.

$$Mo(CO)_6 + 3 \text{ pyridine} \rightarrow Mo(CO)_3py + 3CO$$
$$Fe(CO)_5 + 2PR_3 \rightarrow Fe(CO)_3(PR_3)_2 + 2CO$$

The solution of a carbonyl in alkali results in the formation of carbonyl hydrides. The hydrides are weak acids, and the salt of the acid can be isolated from solution.

$$Fe(CO)_5 + 3OH^- \rightarrow HFe(CO)_4^- + CO_3^{2-} + H_2O$$

Carbonyl halides may result by the direct reaction of a carbonyl with a halogen, although they are more generally prepared by the reaction of the metal halide with carbon monoxide in the presence of a metal such as copper.

$$ReCl_5 + 4Cu + 5CO \rightarrow Re(CO)_5Cl + 4CuCl$$

Structures

It is interesting to note that the simple monomolecular carbonyls have a composition such that the sum of the electrons of the metal and the total electrons contributed by carbon monoxide equal the number of electrons in the rare gas of the period in which the metal resides. Such compounds or ions are said to have an effective atomic number (ean) of a rare gas. This is illustrated in Table 5–7. Note that the monomers for the elements with an odd number of electrons are missing and that these elements only have compounds which are polymers.

The structures of the simple carbonyls can be related to the metal orbitals available for ligand electron occupancy. By simply making use of the Pauling valence bond theory of hydbridized orbitals (Table 5–7), the tetrahedral, $Ni(CO)_4$, trigonal bipyramidal, $Fe(CO)_5$, and octahedral, $M(CO)_6$ structures can be accounted for. The bonding must be somewhat more complicated since the metal-carbon distances are shorter than expected for a single bond. This is accounted for by having some of the electron cloud of the paired metal electrons overlap with the unoccupied higher orbitals of the carbon monoxide to provide partial double bond

Table 5–7
Electron Accounting in Some Volatile Metal Carbonyls

| Compound | Electrons Contributed | | | Orbital Use $(n-1)dnsnp$ | |
	Metal	CO	Total	metal	ligand
$Ni(CO)_4$	28	8	36	o o o o o | x x x x o o o o o | x x x x tetrahedral	sp^3
$Fe(CO)_5$	26	10	36	o o o o | x x x x x o o o o | x x x x x trigonal bipyramid	dsp^3
$Cr(CO)_6$	24	12	36	o o o | x x x x x x o o o | x x x x x x octahedral	d^2sp^3

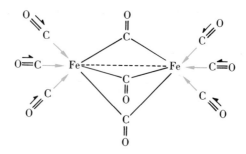

Figure 5–14   Structure of Fe₂(CO)₉.

character.   The polynuclear carbonyls require a more complex structure and involve bridging carbonyls in $Fe_2(CO)_9$ and metal-metal bonds in $Mn_2(CO)_{10}$ (Figures 5–14 and 5–15).

5–6   ORGANOMETALLIC COMPOUNDS

The whole field of transitional element–carbon compounds has developed since 1951.   Before that year only the transitional metal carbonyls and a few compounds of the platinum metals with unsaturated hydrocarbons were known.   Since the first discovery, the

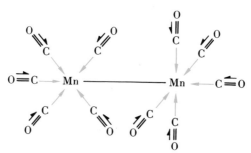

Figure 5–15   Structure of Mn₂(CO)₁₀.

field has grown so rapidly that only a brief survey of types of compounds can be presented here.

Sandwich Compounds

P. L. Pauson, an English chemist, unexpectedly prepared the first of these compounds in the reaction of iron (II) chloride with a Grignard reagent prepared from cyclopentadiene. The reaction is represented by the following equation:

$$FeCl_2 + 2C_5H_5MgBr \xrightarrow[\text{solvent}]{} Fe(C_5H_5)_2 + 2MgBrCl$$

The product $Fe(C_5H_5)_2$, commonly called ferrocene, was isolated as an orange crystalline material. It has a melting point of 174° and is stable to 470°. It is stable to oxidation by air and when oxidized by nitrate ion, yields the blue cation $Fe(C_5H_5)_2^+$. It is stable to hydrolysis in acids and bases. The structure was determined to consist of two staggered cyclopentadienyl radicals with an iron atom sandwiched in between them (Figure 5–16). Compounds of this type have been prepared for most all of the transitional elements; some of these are listed in Table 5–8. The iron compound is the most stable of them all, with the neutral compounds of the $3d$ elements declining in their air stability in the order Ni > Co > V ≫ Cr ∼ Ti.

The bonding in these compounds is difficult to describe in a qualitative way. Although these compounds could be considered

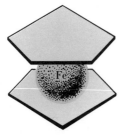

Figure 5–16   Structure of ferrocene.

Table 5-8
Some Examples of Sandwich Compounds of the Transitional Elements

	mp°	Color		Mp°	Color
Cyclopentadienyl (Cp) Derivatives					
$(Cp)_2Ti$	$>130°$	green	$(Cp)_2Ni$	$174°$	bright green
$(Cp)_2V$	$168°$	purple	$(Cp)_2TiBr_2$	$314°$	dark red
$(Cp)_2Cr$	$173°$	scarlet	$(Cp)_2ZrBr_2$	$260°d$	colorless
$(Cp)_2Mn$	$173°$	brown	$(Cp)_2NbBr_3$	$260°d$	dk. red-brown
$(Cp)_2Fe$	$174°$	orange	$(Cp)_2TaBr_3$	$280°d$	rust
$(Cp)_2Co$	$173°$	violet black	$(Cp)_2ReH$	$162°$	
Other Aromatic Systems					
$(C_6H_6)_2V$	$277°$	red brown	sym. $[(CH_3)_3(C_6H_3)]_2M^+$		red
$(C_6H_6)_2Cr$	$284°$	brown-black	Where M is Fe, Os, Ru, Ir, and Rh		
$(C_6H_6)_2Mo$	$115°d$	green			
Mixed Systems					
$CpV(CO)_4$	$138°$	orange	$(C_6H_6)Cr(CO)_3$	$162°$	yellow
$[CpCr(CO)_3]_2$	$163°$	yellow	$(C_6H_6)CoCp$	$227°d$	orange
$[CpW(CO)_3H]$	$66°$	yellow	$(CH_3C_5H_4)Mn(C_6H_6)$	$116°$	ruby-red

as derived from an Fe^{2+} ion and two $C_5H_5^-$ ions, the structures and properties are more related to a molecular species than a group of ions. The compound is diamagnetic, and this corresponds to an electron configuration in which the d^6 electrons of Fe(II) are paired up in three of the d orbitals, thus leaving two of the d orbitals vacant, Fe^{2+} ↿⇂ ↿⇂ ↿⇂ __ __. Each cyclopentadienyl radical has 26 electrons, 10 of which are involved in C—H electron pair bonds, and another 10 in the C—C electron pair bonds. This leaves three pairs, and these are in three orbitals which belong to the molecule as a whole. One pair of these three electron pairs has the correct directional properties to overlap one of the empty d orbitals of the Fe(II) ion. A second cyclopentadienyl radical when parallel to and directly above the first also has one pair of electrons with the correct directional properties to overlap the second empty d orbital of the Fe(II) ion. The net effect is that the iron is effectively bonded to the two cyclopentadienyl radicals by electron pair bonds. As in the simple carbonyls, this compound and many others of this class have an effective atomic number of a rare gas.

Other organic ring systems were soon found to form analogous compounds. Actually F. Hein obtained products (1919) of the composition $Cr(C_6H_5)_n$ which are now recognized as sandwich compounds in which the aromatic compound biphenyl C_6H_5—C_6H_5 (Figure 5–17) forms a sandwich with another molecule of biphenyl or one of benzene. At the time of their discovery they were considered to be simply phenyl groups bonded to chromium with conventional electron pair bonds.

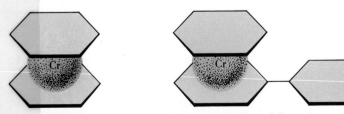

Figure 5–17 Structures of benzenebiphenylchromium and dibenzene chromium.

A general method of preparation for these compounds is represented by the following equations:

$$3MCl_3 + AlCl_3 + 2Al + 6 \frac{Aromatic}{Hydrocarbon} \rightarrow 3M(Ar)_2Al\ Cl_4$$

$$2M(Ar)_2AlCl_4 + S_2O_4{}^{2-} + 4OH^- \rightarrow 2M(Ar)_2 + 2H_2O + 2SO_3{}^{2-} + 2AlCl_3 + 2Cl^-$$

Some of the organic compounds for which this kind of reaction is known are toluene, $C_6H_5CH_3$; ortho, meta, and para xylene, $C_6H_4(CH_3)_2$; meistylene, sym. $C_6H_3(CH_3)_3$; and biphenyl, C_6H_5—C_6H_5; among others. Examples of these compounds are given in Table 5–8 along with a few examples of mixed sandwich compounds and carbonyls also containing an aromatic ring system.

Metal Alkyls

Compounds which have a normal electron pair bond between the carbon and transitional metal have been very difficult to prepare. However, during the past ten years they have been studied intensively by organic and inorganic chemists as well, since they have been found to be important as catalysts in the low temperature polymerization of ethylene and propylene. In fact, two Italian workers in the field, G. Natta and K. Ziegler, were awarded the Nobel prize in chemistry for their accomplishments.

Transitional metal alkyls are formed in, and can be isolated from, reaction systems which consist of a transitional metal anhydrous halide of Group IV, V, or VI and an alkyl of an active metal such as aluminum, $Al(isobutyl)_3$, for instance, in a solvent such as cyclohexane. The intermediates from such a reaction system have the composition $R_2M_tCl_2AlR_2$, where R is the organic radical, and M_t is the transitional metal. In the course of such studies, it was found that the compound $(CH_3)_2TiCl_2$ could be prepared and that it could be used in place of the aluminum compound. The equation for the reaction by which it may be prepared is:

$$(CH_3)_2AlCl + 2TiCl_3 \rightarrow 2CH_3TiCl_2 + AlCl_3$$

This compound is a violet crystalline solid which melts at 28° with decomposition.   A more stable compound can be prepared in which cyclopentadienyl rings replace the chloro groups.

$$(Cp)_2TiCl_2 + 2CH_3MgBr \rightarrow Cp_2Ti(CH_3)_2 + 2MgClBr$$

This is also a violet compound, but it is stable to air and water. This compound in the presence of an aluminum alkyl in organic solvents forms compounds of the type $(Cp)_2TiCl_2AlR_2$.   These compounds have structures in which the cyclopentadienyl rings are at an angle of 150° or more from each other (Figures 5–18a, 5–18b).

Catalysts similar to these may be used in the hydrogenation of unsaturated hydrocarbons under mild conditions of temperature and pressure.   Examples of such compounds are $(i-C_4H_9)_3Al$—$Zr(Cp)_2Cl_2$ and $(i-C_4H_9)_3Al$—$Mn(acetylacetonato)_3$.   Presumably

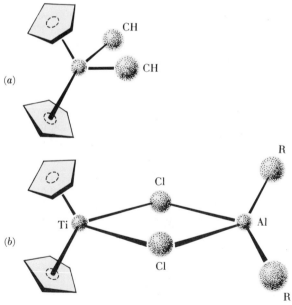

Figure 5–18a   Probable structure of $Cp_2Ti(CH_3)_2$.
Figure 5–18b   Structure of $Cp_2TiCl_2Al(R)_2$.

these compounds have structures similar to that described in Figure 5–18b.

Completely fluorinated hydrocarbons react with metal derivatives (especially carbonyls) to give stable products in which a carbon is bonded to the metal with a normal electron pair bond. Examples of these reactions follow:

$$2C_2F_4 + Fe(CO)_5 \rightarrow (CO)_4Fe\overline{CF_2CF_2CF_2CF}_2 + CO$$
$$CF_2{=}CFCF_2Cl + NaMn(CO)_5 \rightarrow (CO)_5MnCF{=}CFCF_3 + NaCl$$
$$C_3F_7I + Fe(CO)_5 \rightarrow C_3F_7Fe(CO)_4I + CO$$

These compounds in general are volatile solids or liquids which are air-stable and unaffected by moisture. The iodides are the least stable in this respect.

Olefin Compounds

The reaction of ethylene with platinum (II), palladium (II), silver (I), and copper (I) salts has long been known. Zeise isolated compounds such as $(C_2H_4PtCl_2)_2$, $PtCl_2(C_2H_4)_2$, and $C_2H_4PtCl^-$ ion in 1830. It is now known that the ethylene groups are perpendicular to the plane bearing the other ligands (Figure 5–19). The bond involves the donation of electrons from a filled metal d orbital to the vacant antibonding orbital of the ethylene and also the acceptance of the electrons of the double bond by a vacant metal d orbital. Similar compounds are formed with cyclic olefins such as 1,5, hexadiene in the compound $(C_6H_{10})PtCl_2$.

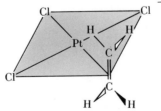

Figure 5–19   Structure of $PtCl_3(C_2H_4)^-$ ion.

This kind of bonding also occurs in acetylenic compounds such as $(Bu_tC{\equiv}CBu_t)_2PtCl_2$, where Bu_t stands for tertiary butyl group. The compound $(C_6H_5)_3Cr(THF)_3$, where THF is tetrahydrofuran, is a catalyst for the polymerization of acetylenes to various benzene derivatives.

$$3RC{\equiv}CR \xrightarrow{(C_6H_5)_3Cr(THF)_3} R-\underset{\underset{R \quad R}{|\quad|}}{\overset{\overset{R \quad R}{|\quad|}}{\bigcirc}}-R$$

These examples serve to dramatize the importance of transitional element chemistry in organic synthesis. The existence of these compounds also tends to break down the artificial separation of organic and inorganic chemistry and provides a basis for the unification of the subject matter.

Appendix

A–1   WRITING NET EQUATIONS

THE CHEMICAL REACTIONS in aqueous solution are described by net equations. In a net equation only the formulas for the major species, i.e., those present in the highest concentrations of reactants and products are included. In acid solution the major hydrogen species are H^+ and H_2O, in basic solution OH^- is used in place of H^+. The net equation does not represent a mechanism of a reaction, but only shows those species which disappear and appear. The net equation does not include the dissolution mechanism of the solid. The assumption is made that the species of which the solid is constituted are instantaneously dispersed in the solvent. Therefore the net equation is related to the equilibrium established between the various species in solution.

By convention, all insoluble compounds, weakly dissociated compounds, and gases are written in molecular form. This should not be taken to mean that insoluble compounds are necessarily molecular in the solid state. The following examples will illustrate these points.

The solution of manganese in a strong acid is given by

$$Mn + 2H^+ \rightarrow Mn^{2+} + H_2$$

while the solution of scandium in a weak acid is written as

$$2Sc + 6CH_3COOH \rightarrow 2Sc^{3+} + 6CH_3COO^- + 3H_2$$

A net equation involving an oxidation-reduction reaction is illustrated by the solution of copper in dilute nitric acid

$$3Cu + 8H^+ + 2NO_3^- \rightarrow 3Cu^{2+} + 2NO + 4H_2O$$

The solution of insoluble silver chloride in aqueous ammonia is given by

$$AgCl + 2NH_3 \rightarrow Ag(NH_3)_2^+ + Cl^-$$

and the solubility of iron (II) sulfide in strong acid by

$$FeS + 2H^+ \rightarrow Fe^{2+} + H_2S$$

As an example of reactions occurring in basic solution, the reaction of sulfite ion with water may be used,

$$SO_3^{2-} + H_2O \rightleftarrows HSO_3^- + OH^-$$

and the solution of chromium hydroxide in strong base

$$Cr(OH)_3 + OH^- \rightarrow Cr(OH)_4^-$$

A–2   WRITING EQUILIBRIUM CONSTANTS

The reaction represented by the equation

$$Fe(H_2O)_6^{3+} + H_2O \rightleftarrows Fe(OH)(H_2O)_5^{2+} + H_3O^+$$

for all practical purposes occurs instantaneously to yield a specific concentration of each species. Although the final concentrations are constant, the system is not static, but dynamic. That is, the product species are continuously reforming reactant species, and the reactant species are constantly forming product species. This is indicated by using two oppositely directed arrows in the equation. When the rates of the forward process and the reverse process are the same, the final concentrations remain constant with time. The system is said to be at equilibrium. At constant temperature, the product of the equilibrium concentrations of the product species when each raised to the power equal to the coefficient of the species in the balanced equation, divided by the product of the equilibrium concentration of the reacting species also raised to the appropriate power, ideally yields a constant called the equilibrium constant. The concentration of the solvent water is assumed to be constant and therefore does not enter into the expression. For the previous equation the expression is written as follows,

$$\frac{[Fe(OH)H_2O^{2+}][H_3O^+]}{[Fe(H_2O)_6^{3+}]} = K_1 \qquad \text{(A-1)}$$

Ideally the magnitude of this constant is dependent solely upon the specific ions involved and the temperature. However, this is only approximately true, because in all but the most dilute solutions the influence of the ions on one another changes their effective concentrations. The net effect is that the quotient is dependent upon concentration. If the data are available, corrections are made for these effects by multiplying the molar concentrations by factors called activity coefficients. The constant thus obtained is not dependent upon concentrations. Unfortunately, not all the data reported in the literature are true equilibrium constants, but rather equilibrium quotients determined at specific concentrations of electrolyte. Care must be taken to compare equilibrium quotients which were determined under similar conditions of electrolyte concentration.

The symbols K_1, K_2, etc. refer to the successive equilibrium constants for the formation of complex ions with anions of strong acids. For example (although only the symbol of the ion has been written here, the ions are all hydrated),

$$Fe^{3+} + Cl^- \rightleftarrows FeCl^{2+} \qquad K_1 = \frac{[FeCl^{2+}]}{[Fe^{3+}][Cl^-]} \qquad \text{(A-2)}$$

$$FeCl^{2+} + Cl^- \rightleftarrows FeCl_2^+ \qquad K_2 = \frac{[FeCl_2^+]}{[FeCl^{2+}][Cl^-]} \qquad \text{(A-3)}$$

When an anion of a weak acid is involved, the equation takes the form,

$$Fe^{3+} + HF \rightleftarrows FeF^{2+} + H^+ \qquad K_1^* = \frac{[FeF^{2+}][H^+]}{[Fe^{3+}][HF]}$$
$$\text{(A-4)}$$

The K^* and K are related to one another by the ionization constant for the weak acid, thus $K_1 = K_1^*/K_{HX}$.

A–3 CONVENTIONS FOR STANDARD ELECTRODE POTENTIALS

Consider the reaction of zinc metal with hydrogen ions and the reaction of hydrogen gas with copper ions as represented by the equations:

$$Zn_{(s)} + 2H^+_{(aq)} \rightarrow Zn^{2+}_{(aq)} + H_{2(g)}$$
$$Cu^{2+}_{(aq)} + H_{2(g)} \rightarrow Cu_{(s)} + 2H^+_{(aq)}$$

These complete reactions may be separated into half-reactions (called couples), which for comparison purposes are all written as reduction reactions.

$$Zn^{2+}_{(aq)} + 2e \rightarrow Zn_{(s)}$$
$$2H^+_{(aq)} + 2e \rightarrow H_{2(g)}$$
$$Cu^{2+}_{(aq)} + 2e \rightarrow Cu_{(s)}$$

Now by convention, an energy value (in volts) relative to the hydrogen-ion-hydrogen-gas couple is assigned, which is positive for a couple in which the oxidized form of the couple is reduced by hydrogen gas. Alternately, this means that the reduced form of the couple will not be oxidized by hydrogen ions. More generally the oxidized form of a couple will oxidize the reduced form of any couple with a value less positive than its own. Similarly, a negative value is assigned to the potential of a couple in which the reduced form of the couple reduces hydrogen ions to hydrogen gas. This is the same as saying that hydrogen ions are capable of oxidizing the reduced form of the couple. In more general terms, the reduced form of a couple will reduce the oxidized form of any couple which stands below it in the table. The standard electrode potentials for the transitional elements are tabulated in Tables 4–9 and 4–10.

From the standard electrode potentials, predictions can be made as to whether or not a reaction will progress spontaneously. The half-reactions can be summed or subtracted algebraically, and if the complete reaction is obtained from the two half-reactions, then the voltage values are simply added or subtracted just as the half-reactions are, for example:

$$Cu^{2+}_{(aq)} + 2e \rightarrow Cu_{(s)} + 0.34$$
$$\underline{Zn^{2+}_{(aq)} + 2e \rightarrow Zn_{(s)} - 0.76}$$
$$Cu^{2+}_{(aq)} + Zn_{(s)} \rightarrow Cu_{(s)} + Zn^{2+}_{(aq)} + 1.10 \text{ volts}$$

A positive value means that the reaction will proceed as written. If, however, two half-reactions are added or subtracted to produce a third half-reaction, then each voltage value must be multiplied by the number of electrons transferred and the sum divided by the number of electrons which appear in the third half-reaction; for example

$$
\begin{array}{ll}
\text{Mn}^{3+}_{(aq)} + 1e \rightarrow \text{Mn}^{2+}_{(aq)} & -1.5(1) \\
\text{Mn}^{2+}_{(aq)} + 2e \rightarrow \text{Mn}_{(s)} & -1.18(2) \\
\hline
\text{Mn}^{3+}_{(aq)} + 3e \rightarrow \text{Mn}_{(s)} & \dfrac{-1.5 + (-1.18)(2)}{3} \\
& = -1.29 \text{ volts}
\end{array}
$$

In the solution chemistry discussed in Chapter IV, we were particularly interested in water as an oxidizing agent and a reducing agent over a range of hydrogen ion concentrations. Although the potential for the $2\text{H}^{+}_{(aq)} + 2e \rightarrow \text{H}_{2(g)}$ half-reaction is set equal to 0.00 when the hydrogen gas pressure is one atmosphere and the hydrogen ion concentration is 1 molal, at other concentrations its value must be other than zero. The relationship between the potential for a half-cell at nonstandard conditions and its value under standard conditions is given by the equation

$$
E = E^{\circ} - \frac{0.059}{n} \log K \tag{A-5}
$$

where n is the number of electrons involved in the reaction, and K is in the form of the equilibrium quotient for the reaction.

For example, in the half-reaction

$$
2\text{H}^{+} + 2e \rightarrow \text{H}_2
$$

the value of $E = E^{\circ} - \dfrac{0.059}{2} \log \dfrac{p_{\text{H}_2}}{(\text{H}^{+})^2}$

$$
= E^{\circ} - 0.059 \log \frac{1}{(\text{H}^{+})}
$$

at 1 atmosphere H_2 gas. Thus,

$$
E = E^{\circ} - 0.059\text{pH} \tag{A-6}
$$

Therefore with each unit increase of pH, the E values become more negative by 0.059 volts (Table A-1).

Table A-1
E Values for the $H^+ + 2e \rightarrow H_2$ Reaction in Acid or $2H_2O + 2e^- \rightarrow H_2 + OH^-$ in Base as a Function of pH

pH	$-E$	pH	$-E$	pH	$-E$
0	0.00	5	0.295	10	0.596
1	0.059	6	0.345	11	0.655
2	0.118	7	0.419	12	0.714
3	0.177	8	0.478	13	0.773
4	0.236	9	0.537	14	0.826

Consequently, hydrogen gas becomes a stronger reducing agent as the hydrogen ion concentration decreases or, looking at it in the reverse, water becomes a stronger oxidizing agent as the hydrogen ion concentration increases.

The other important half-reaction in water solution is the oxygen-water reaction:

$$\text{Acid} \quad O_2 + 4H^+ + 4e^- \rightarrow 2H_2O$$
$$\text{Base} \quad O_2 + 2H_2O + 4e^- \rightarrow 4OH^-$$

At standard conditions in acid solution, $E°$ is 1.23 volts. The equation as written shows oxygen gas as the oxidizing agent, while in the reverse reaction, water is a reducing agent. Since this reaction is also dependent upon the hydrogen ion concentration, the value of E again varies with the pH.

$$E = E° - \frac{0.059}{4} \log \frac{1}{p_{O_2}(H^+)^4}$$
$$E = E° - 0.059 \log pH/p_{O_2} \qquad \text{(A–7)}$$

The values for the electrode potential at each pH are given in Table A–2. Thus oxygen gas becomes a poorer oxidizing agent as the solution becomes more basic, or to put it another way, water becomes a better reducing agent as the solution becomes more

Table A–2

E Values for the $O_2 + 4H^+ + 4e \rightarrow 2H_2O$
Reaction in Acid or $O_2 + 2H_2O + 4e \rightarrow 4OH$ in Base
as a Function of pH

pH	E	pH	E	pH	E
0	1.23	5	0.935	10	0.640
1	1.17	6	0.876	11	0.581
2	1.11	7	0.817	12	0.522
3	1.05	8	0.758	13	0.463
4	0.994	9	0.699	14	0.404

basic. A plot of the data in Tables A–1 and A–2 is given in Figure 4–3.

When dealing with oxygen gas as an oxidizing agent under normal conditions of one-fifth of an atmosphere pressure rather than one atmosphere, this change in concentration must be corrected for accordingly. For example, the E value at 1 molal hydrogen ion, but $\frac{1}{5}$ atmosphere of oxygen pressure, is equal to

$$1.23 - \frac{0.059}{n} \log \frac{1}{(0.2)}$$

$$= 1.23 - \frac{0.059}{4}(0.699)$$

$$= 1.23 - 0.01$$

$$= 1.22$$

A–4 NOMENCLATURE OF COMPLEX COMPOUNDS

1. The ligands are named first, in the order negative, neutral, and positive.
2. Negative ligands all end in -o. Thus Cl^- chloro, SO_4^{2-} sulfato, CO_3^{2-} carbonato, $C_2O_4^{2-}$ oxalato, NO_3^- nitrato, NO_2^- nitrito when O-bonded (nitro when N-bonded), CN^- cyano.
3. The ordinary name of a neutral ligand is used, except that either aquo or aqua may be used for water and ammine is used for the ammonia molecule to distinguish it from organic amines.
4. Positive ligands end in -ium. Thus NO^+ nitronium, $N_2H_3^+$ hydrazinium.

5. The number of coordinating groups is designated by di-, tri-, and tetra-, except for complex organic names where bis-, tris-, and tetrakis- are used to indicate that what follows is a complex name. For example, bis(ethylenediamine) refers to two molecules of $NH_2CH_2CH_2NH_2$ and not ethylene and two ammonia molecules.

6. The name of the central element is given after the ligands have been named. The name of the element itself is used for cationic and neutral species, and the ending -ate is used for *all* anionic species.

7. The oxidation state of the central atom is designated by Roman numerals and is enclosed in parentheses. Zero valent elements are indicated by (0). Thus $Ni(CN)_4^{4-}$ is tetracyanonickelate (0).

8. A bridging group is designated by μ and is repeated before the name of each bridging group.

9. Common abbreviations of organic ligands are:

acetylacetono	$CH_3COCHCOCH_3^-$	acac
oxalato	$C_2O_4^{2-}$	ox
ethylenediamine	$NH_2CH_2CH_2NH_2$	en
pyridine	C_5H_5N	py
cyclopentadienyl radical	$C_5H_5^-$	Cp
ethylenediamine tetraacetic acid		EDTA
substituted phosphines		R_3P
amines		R_3N
sulfides		R_2S

Examples of the rules follow:

$Co(NH_3)_4Cl_2^+$	dichlorotetramminecobalt(III) ion
$Co(NH_2CH_2CH_2NH_2)_2Br_2^+$	dibromobis(ethylenediamine) cobalt(III) ion
$Cr(NH_3)_2(SCN)_4^-$	tetrathiocyanatodiamminechromate(III) anion
$Mo(CN)_8^{4-}$	octacyanomolybdate(IV) anion
$(NH_3)_5Cr(OH)Cr(NH_3)_5^+$	decammine-μ-hydroxodichromium(III) ion

A–5   TABLES OF DATA

Table A–3

Ionization Potentials of Transitional Metal Atoms and Ions*

	Neutral Atom		M^{1+}		M^{2+}	
	Config.	I.P.	Config.	I.P.	Config.	I.P.
Sc	$3d^14s^2$	6.54	$3d^14s^1$	12.80	$3d^1$	24.75
Ti	$3d^24s^2$	6.82	$3d^24s^1$	13.57	$3d^2$	27.47
V	$3d^34s^2$	6.74	$3d^4$	14.65	$3d^3$	29.31
Cr	$3d^54s^1$	6.76	$3d^5$	16.49	$3d^4$	30.95
Mn	$3d^54s^2$	7.43	$3d^54s^1$	15.64	$3d^5$	33.69
Fe	$3d^64s^2$	7.90	$3d^64s^1$	16.18	$3d^6$	30.64
Co	$3d^74s^2$	7.86	$3d^8$	17.05	$3d^7$	33.49
Ni	$3d^84s^2$	7.63	$3d^9$	18.15	$3d^8$	35.16
Cu	$3d^{10}4s^1$	7.72	$3d^{10}$	20.29	$3d^9$	36.83
Zn	$3d^{10}4s^2$	9.39	$3d^{10}4s^1$	17.96	$3d^{10}$	39.70
Y	$4d^15s^2$	6.38	$5s^2$	12.4	$4d^1$	20.5
Zr	$4d^25s^2$	6.84	$4d^25s^1$	13.13	$4d^2$	22.98
Nb	$4d^45s^1$	6.88	$4d^4$	14.32	$4d^3$	25.04
Mo	$4d^55s^1$	7.10	$4d^5$	16.15	$4d^4$	27.13
Tc	$4d^55s^2$	7.28	$4d^55s^1$	15.26	$(4d^5)$	—
Ru	$4d^75s^1$	7.36	$4d^7$	16.76	$4d^6$	28.46
Rh	$4d^85s^1$	7.46	$4d^8$	18.07	$4d^7$	31.05
Pd	$4d^{10}$	8.33	$4d^9$	19.42	$4d^8$	32.92
Ag	$4d^{10}5s^1$	7.57	$4d^{10}$	21.48	$4d^9$	34.82
Cd	$4d^{10}5s^2$	8.99	$4d^{10}5s^1$	16.90	$4d^{10}$	37.47
La	$5d^16s^2$	5.61	$5d^2$	11.43	$5d^1$	19.17
Hf	$5d^26s^2$	(7)	$5d^16s^2$	14.90	$(5d^2)$	—
Ta	$5d^36s^2$	7.88	$5d^36s^1$	(16.2)	$(5d^3)$	—
W	$5d^46s^2$	7.98	$5d^46s^1$	(17.7)	$(5d^4)$	—
Re	$5d^56s^2$	7.87	$5d^56s^1$	(16.6)	$(5d^5)$	—
Os	$5d^66s^2$	8.7	$5d^66s^1$	(17)	$(5d^6)$	—
Ir	$5d^76s^2$	(9)	$(5d^76s^1)$	—	$(5d^7)$	—
Pt	$5d^96s^1$	9.0	$5d^9$	18.56	$(5d^8)$	—
Au	$5d^{10}6s^1$	9.22	$5d^{10}$	20.5	$(5d^9)$	—
Hg	$5d^{10}6s^2$	10.43	$5d^{10}6s^1$	18.75	$(5d^{10})$	—
Ac	$6d^17s^2$	6.9	$7s^2$	12.1	$7s^1$	20
Th	$6d^27s^2$	—	$6d^27s^1$	—	$6d^2$	—

* C. Moore Circular No. 467, National Bureau Standards (1949, 1952, 1956).

Table A–4
Coordination Number 12 Radii (Å) for the Transitional Element Metals

3d	Geller*	Pauling**	4d	Geller	Pauling	5d	Geller	Pauling	4f‡		6d and 5f	
Sc	—	1.6545	Y	—	1.7780	La	—	1.8852	Ceα	1.8248	Ac	1.88†
Ti	1.43	1.47	Zr	1.64	1.60	Hf	—	1.62	Prα	1.8363	Th	1.80‡
V	1.31	1.36	Nb	1.51	1.47	Ta	1.50	1.49	Ndα	1.8290	Pa	—
Cr	1.24	1.30	Mo	1.41	1.39	W	—	1.41	Pm	—	U	—
Mn	—	1.27	Tc	—	1.35	Re	—	1.37	Sm	1.8105	Np	—
Fe	—	1.26	Ru	1.38	1.34	Os	1.36	1.35	Eu	1.994	Pu	—
Co	1.30	1.25	Rh	1.355	1.34	Ir	1.36	1.36	Gd	1.810	Am	1.730
Ni	1.32	1.25	Pd	—	1.37	Pt	1.38	1.39	Tb	1.8005		
Cu	—	1.28	Ag	—	1.44	Au	1.41	1.46	Dy	1.7952		
Zn	—	1.27	Cd	—	1.54	Hg	1.47	1.57	Ho	1.7887		
									Er	1.7794		
									Tm	1.7688		
									Yb	1.9397		
									Lu	1.7516		

* S. Geller, *Acta Cryst.* **9**, 885 (1956)

** L. Pauling, *Nature of the Chemical Bond*, 3rd ed. (Ithaca, New York: Cornell University Press, 1960).

† J. G. Sites, Jr., M. L. Salutsky, and D. B. Stone, *J. Am. Chem. Soc.* **77**, 237 (1958).

‡ F. H. Spedding and A. H. Daane, *The Rare Earths* (New York: John Wiley and Sons, 1961).

Table A–5

Coordination Number Six Radii (Å) for the Ions of the $3d$*§ $4f$† and $5f$‡ Elements

Number of Electrons	d^0	d^1	d^2	d^3	d^4	d^5	d^6	d^7	d^8	d^9	d^{10}
	Sc^{3+} 0.686	Ti^{3+} 0.633	V^{3+} 0.625	Cr^{3+} 0.608	Mn^{3+} 0.625	Fe^{3+} 0.628	Co^{3+} 0.56	—	—	—	—
		—	Ti^{2+} 0.80	V^{2+} 0.73	Cr^{2+} —	Mn^{2+} 0.90	Fe^{2+} 0.85	Co^{2+} 0.80	Ni^{2+} 0.76	Cu^{2+} 0.80	Zn^{2+} 0.83

Number of Electrons	f^1	f^2	f^3	f^4	f^5	f^6	f^7	f^8	f^9	f^{10}	f^{11}	f^{12}	f^{13}	f^{14}
	Ce^{3+} 1.034	Pr^{3+} 1.013	Nd^{3+} 0.995	Pm^{3+} (0.979)	Sm^{3+} 0.964	Eu^{3+} 0.950	Gd^{3+} 0.938	Tb^{3+} 0.923	Dy^{3+} 0.908	Ho^{3+} 0.894	Er^{3+} 0.881	Tm^{3+} 0.869	Yb^{3+} 0.858	Lu^{3+} 0.848
	(Th^{3+}) (1.08)	(Pa^{3+}) (1.05)	U^{3+} 1.03	Np^{3+} 1.01	Pu^{3+} 1.00	Am^{3+} 0.99	Cm^{3+} 0.98							

* S. Geller, *Acta Cryst.* **10**, 248 (1957).
§ N. Hush and M. Pryce, *J. Chem. Phys.* **26**, 143 (1957).
† D. H. Templeton and C. H. Dauben, *J. Am. Chem. Soc.* **76**, 5237 (1954).
‡ W. H. Zachariasen, Ch. 18, *Actinide Elements*, N.N.E.S. Div. IV, 14 A (1954).

Table A-6
The Magnetic Moments of the Ions of the $3d$* and $4f$** Elements

Number of Electrons	d^1	d^2	d^3	d^4	d^5	d^6	d^7	d^8	d^9
Ion Exptl*	Ti^{3+}	V^{3+}	Cr^{3+}	Cr^{2+}	Mn^{2+}	Fe^{2+}	Co^{2+}	Ni^{2+}	Cu^{2+}
	1.73	2.75	3.70	4.75	5.62	5.10	4.30	2.80	1.70
		2.85	3.90	4.90	6.10	5.70	5.20	3.50	2.20
Theory— (Spin only / Spin-free)	1.73	2.83	3.88	4.90	5.92	4.40	3.88	2.83	1.73

Number of Electrons	f^1	f^2	f^3	f^4	f^5	f^6	f^7	f^8	f^9	f^{10}	f^{11}	f^{12}	f^{13}
Ion	Ce^{3+}	Pr^{3+}	Nd^{3+}	Pm^{3+}	Sm^{3+}	Eu^{3+}	Gd^{3+}	Tb^{3+}	Dy^{3+}	Ho^{3+}	Er^{3+}	Tm^{3+}	Yb^{3+}
Exptl**	2.46	3.47	3.52	—	1.58	3.54	7.9	9.6	10.3	10.4	9.4	7.0	4.3
Theory	2.56	3.62	3.68	2.83	1.55	3.40	7.94	9.7	10.6	10.6	9.6	7.6	4.5
					1.65	3.51							

* J. Lewis and R. G. Wilkins, *Modern Coordination Chemistry* (New York: Wiley-Interscience, 1960), p. 406.

** F. H. Spedding and A. H. Daane, *The Rare Earths* (New York: John Wiley and Sons, 1961), p. 13.

A–6   REFERENCE MATERIALS

GENERAL

E. Cartmell and G. W. A. Fowles, *Valency and Molecular Structure* (2nd ed., London: Butterworths, 1961).

K. B. Harvey and G. B. Porter, *Introduction to Physical Inorganic Chemistry* (Reading, Massachusetts: Addison-Wesley, 1963).

F. A. Cotton and G. Wilkinson, *Advanced Inorganic Chemistry* (New York: Wiley-Interscience, 1962).

R. B. Heslop and P. L. Robinson, *Inorganic Chemistry* (2nd ed., Amsterdam: Elsevier, 1963).

J. Kleinberg, W. J. Argersinger, Jr., and E. Griswold, *Inorganic Chemistry* (Boston: D. C. Heath and Co., 1960).

E. S. Gould, *Inorganic Reactions and Structure* (Revised ed. New York: Holt, Rinehart and Winston, 1962).

R. Sanderson, *Chemical Periodicity* (New York: Reinhold, 1960).

N. V. Sidgwick, *The Chemical Elements and Their Compounds*, Vols. I and II (London: Oxford University Press, 1960).

THE ACTINIDES

Glenn T. Seaborg, *Man-Made Transuranum Elements* (Englewood Cliffs, N.J.: Prentice-Hall, 1963).

SOLUTION CHEMISTRY

J. P. Hunt, *Metal Ions in Aqueous Solution* (New York: W. A. Benjamin, 1963).

THE HALIDES

S. Y. Tyree, Jr., "Anhydrous Metal Chlorides," *Inorganic Syntheses* Vol. 7, J. Kleinberg, ed., (New York: McGraw-Hill, 1963).

COORDINATION CHEMISTRY

L. E. Orgel, *An Introduction to Transition-Metal Chemistry* (New York: John Wiley and Sons, 1960).

J. Lewis and R. G. Wilkins, *Modern Coordination Chemistry* (New York: Wiley-Interscience Publishers, 1960).

F. Basolo and R. G. Pearson, *Mechanisms of Inorganic Reactions* (New York: John Wiley and Sons, 1958).

The Chemistry of Coordination Compounds, J. Bailer, ed. (American Chemical Society Monograph No. 131) (New York: Reinhold, 1956).

H. Taube, "Rates and Mechanisms of Substitution in Inorganic Complexes in Solution," *Chem. Rev.* **50** (1952) 60–126.

F. Basolo, "Stereochemistry and Reaction Mechanisms of Hexacovalent Inorganic Complexes," *Chem. Rev.* **52** (1953) 459–527.

ORGANOMETALLIC COMPOUNDS

G. Wilkinson, and F. A. Cotton in *Progress in Inorganic Chemistry*, F. A. Cotton, ed., Vol. 1 (New York: Wiley-Interscience, 1959).

H. P. Fritz and E. O. Fisher in *Advances in Inorganic Chemistry & Radiochemistry*, Vol. 1, H. J. Emeleus and A. G. Sharpe, eds. (New York: Academic, 1959).

SOLID STATE

W. E. Addison, *Structural Principles in Inorganic Compounds* (England: T. A. Constable, 1961).

Leonid V. Azaroff, *Introduction to Solids* (New York: McGraw-Hill, 1960).

A. F. Wells, *Structural Inorganic Chemistry*, 3rd ed. (England: Oxford University Press, 1963).

W. G. Gehman, "Standard Ionic Crystal Structures," *J. Chem. Ed.* **40**, (1963) 54–63.

PHYSICAL DATA

Chemistry and Metallurgy of Miscellaneous Materials: Thermodynamics, L. L. Quill, ed. (New York: McGraw-Hill, 1950).

F. A. Rossini, et al., *Selected Values of Chemical Thermodynamics Properties*, National Bureau of Standards Circular 500, 1952.

L. Brewer, "Thermodynamic Properties of the Oxides and Their Vaporization Processes," *Chem. Rev.* **52** (1953) 1–75.

Joint Army, Navy, Air-Force Interim Thermodynamic Tables (Midland, Michigan: Dow Chemical, 1960, revised periodically).

Index